**Chemical
Equilibrium
and
Solutions**

A Programmed Introduction

Programmed Units in General Chemistry

Chemical Equilibrium and Solutions

A PROGRAMMED INTRODUCTION

Lieutenant Colonel James E. Banks

United States Air Force Academy
Tenure Associate Professor of Chemistry

McGraw-Hill Book Company

New York   St. Louis   San Francisco   Toronto   London   Sydney

Chemical Equilibrium and Solutions
A Programmed Introduction

preface

About this book

This book has been written to help you learn the vocabulary, concepts, and problem-solving skills associated with the subjects of chemical equilibrium, Le Châtelier's principle, solutions, and aqueous solutions of electrolytes. The chapters are arranged to correspond to the usual chapter coverage of other textbooks, and a list of references to some of these is provided at the end of each chapter. Within each chapter and section, however, factual material appears as it is needed to build understanding.

An unusual feature of the book is that it is programmed; facts and concepts have been organized to require you to respond to them so that in a sense you are participating in formulating the very ideas the book teaches you. Also, facts are presented in a sequence that corresponds to your learning progression, and your grasp of each point is tested before you go to the next.

The book employs the technique of semiprogramming to present some topics in general chemistry. I have used this format because it combines the good features of a regular textbook with the step-by-step approach of programmed instruction; that is, I have used the narrative, discursive medium for descriptive material and introductions to new concepts, together with a programmed medium for teaching discriminations and applying concepts.

What this book will (and won't) do for you

Your first study of chemistry may seem like the first few weeks of class in a foreign language because there are many new words to learn and even more new meanings for old familiar words. Until you master them, you can't go on to the really exciting and interesting phases of chemistry. If you let it, this book will familiarize you with quite a few of these new terms and meanings as well as the ideas they express.

Using this program will be work—there is no easy road to learning chemistry—but you will find that you can test your progress as you go along. I have tried to emphasize the subjects that may give you trouble and to bridge the minor pitfalls so you can avoid them.

The problems you solve as you study this book are typical of those you will face on homework assignments, quizzes, and examinations. Since you won't have to go on until you fully understand how to work a problem, your confidence will increase as you proceed.

How to use this book

You should start this book just as if you were reading a regular text. After a few paragraphs, however, you will encounter the frames that make up the programmed sections of the book. By responding with your own word or phrase to complete the meaning of a phrase, you prove to yourself that you understand what you have read.

As you can see, the correct answer is written at the right-hand side of the page. If you have the right answer, go on to the next frame; if you miss the question, you should be able to see your mistake before you go further.

There are some frames which require you to calculate. For example,

If you paid $5.00 for a book with 863 pages, what was
the cost per page?_____ $0.0058

A frame of this type may be followed by several more which go through a step-by-step solution of the problem. If you get the problem right the first time, you can skip these explanatory frames.

Finally, there are some more involved questions or problems for which you have a choice of responses. Think carefully before you make a choice and then refer to the paragraph indicated.

If there are 49 red marbles and 18 blue marbles in a bag, what is the minimum number you must take out to be certain of having two of the same color?

If your answer is 2   Go to A below
If your answer is 3   Go to B below
If you need help   Go to C below

A
_____

You are wrong. If you do choose a wrong answer, you will find an analysis of your mistake and some help in correcting it.

B
_____

Right. When you pick the correct answer, you find out immediately and are ordinarily directed to proceed to the next section.

C

If you pick a response such as this, you will usually find a detailed review of the point in question and some additional examples to help you understand it.

At the end of the text you will find brief tests to help you evaluate your mastery of the material in each chapter. They are not exhaustive, but are representative of the kind of problem you should be able to handle easily after working through the chapter. If you find them difficult or if you make many errors, you should review appropriate sections of the text.

In working this program, avoid careless answers. If you find yourself making mistakes because you are tired or your attention is wandering, take a rest. If you put the program aside for a few days, it is a good idea to review a few pages before you begin new material.

James E. Banks

contents

**Chemical
Equilibrium
and
Solutions**

A Programmed Introduction

Programmed Units in General Chemistry

chapter one # chemical equilibrium

1.1 Chemical reactions

Chemistry is the science of matter and its transformations. Every day we see examples of these transformations. The rusting of iron is one. Iron itself is a hard, dense solid with a metallic sheen. When it is exposed to moist air, a slow change takes place. Rust, the flaky, reddish powder we all know, gradually forms on the surface. If the iron is exposed long enough, it will all be converted to rust.

The rusting of iron is an example of a chemical change, which may be defined as *any change in matter that results in the disappearance of one or more substances, and the appearance of one or more new substances, each with its own set of chemical properties.* Modern life depends on chemical changes such as the combustion of gasoline in car engines, the conversion of ores to pure metals, and the synthesis of plastics from other less exotic substances.

We must, however, be careful to distinguish chemical changes, in which new substances are formed, from physical changes which involve only a physical rearrangement of material or a change in its physical state. When water boils or evaporates, no new substance is formed. There is no chemical change. Likewise, grinding sugar crystals to a fine powder is only a physical change.

All chemical changes obey two rules. The first is the *law of conservation of mass:* In any chemical reaction the initial weight of the reacting substances is equal to the final weight of the products. The second rule is known as the *law of definite proportions:* When two or more elements combine, they always do so in a fixed, or definite, proportion by weight.

The course of a chemical reaction is represented by a chemical equation, which tells the substances involved in the reaction and makes it possible to determine the relative weights which react. It may also indicate the physical state of the substances—whether each is a solid, liquid, or gas. For example,

$$4Fe(s) + 3O_2(g) \rightarrow 2Fe_2O_3(s)$$

is a chemical equation representing the chemical reaction between *solid* iron and *gaseous* oxygen to form *solid* iron oxide.

By agreement among chemists, the substances written to the left of the symbol $\rightarrow$ are called reactants and those to the right are called products. In the reaction represented by the equation above, Fe and O_2 are the reactants; Fe_2O_3 is the product.

Chemists are concerned with the transformations of
_____

matter

In general, transformations of matter can be divided into two categories: _____ and _____ changes.

chemical
physical

A chemical change results in the formation of _____
_____.

(a) new substance(s)

The burning of natural gas is a _____ change because _____ are formed.

chemical
new substances

The melting of ice is an example of a _____
_____ because _____
_____.

physical change;
no new substances
are formed

$H_2(g) + Cl_2(g) \rightarrow 2HCl(g)$ is a _____
_____ representing the reaction between H_2 and Cl_2.

chemical equation

In this reaction, H_2 and Cl_2 are the _____;
HCl is the _____.

reactants
product

By experiment it can be found that 2 g of H_2 reacts with 71 g of Cl_2 to form 73 g of HCl. This is an illustration of the law of _____
_____.

conservation of
mass

From the last statement we can calculate that HCl is composed of 2.7% H and 97.3% Cl. According to the law of _____, HCl will always have this percentage composition.

definite proportions

The law of constant composition is another name for _____.

the law of definite proportions

"Matter can be neither created nor destroyed" is one way of expressing the law of _____ _____.

conservation of mass

Which of these equations represents a chemical reaction?

$$CO_2(s) \rightleftharpoons CO_2(g) \qquad or \qquad C(s) + O_2(g) \rightarrow CO_2(g)$$

$C(s) + O_2(g) \rightarrow CO_2(g)$

If 24 g of C reacts completely with 64 g of O_2, _____ g of CO_2 will be formed.

88

When 6 g of C is allowed to react with an excess of O_2, _____ g of CO_2 is formed.

22

1.2 Energy of chemical reactions

Every chemical reaction involves an energy change as well as the formation of new substances. Sometimes energy is needed to bring about a chemical change. For example, heat and light are required for the combination of water and carbon dioxide in plants to form carbohydrates. In other reactions, such as the burning of wood, coal, or gasoline, energy is liberated. From this standpoint, energy may be considered as just another reactant or product of the reaction. When energy is needed to bring about a reaction, it is one of the reactants and the reaction is said to be *endoergic*. On the other hand, when the reaction liberates energy, the energy is a product, and the reaction is termed *exoergic*. There are many kinds of energy. The light and heat which a plant uses in its growth are stored as potential energy until the plant is either burned or eaten. A dry-cell battery is a source of chemical potential energy that can be converted into light (flashlight), mechanical energy (toy boat), sound (doorbell), or heat.

Most chemical reactions involve heat. A reaction which liberates heat is an *exothermic reaction*. One that uses up heat is called an *endothermic reaction*. Both of these words come from the Greek word for "heat," *thermos*. It is important that you understand the meaning and implications of these two terms. Many familiar chemical changes are exothermic reactions; their heat usually causes the surroundings to become warm. The burning of natural gas, for example, is exothermic. The heat which is liberated can be used to warm buildings or make coffee. Endothermic reactions tend to cool off the reacting substances. Both the mixture and its container may become cool to the touch. The combination of carbon and sulfur to form carbon disulfide is an endothermic reaction.

The change in heat content that accompanies a chemical change can be indicated by a *thermochemical equation*. A thermochemical equation differs from an ordinary chemical equation in that it shows whether heat is required to bring about the reaction or is produced by the reaction. Thus, for an exothermic reaction such as the combination of hydrogen and oxygen to produce water,

$$2H_2(g) + O_2(g) \rightarrow 2H_2O(l) + \text{heat}$$

The thermochemical equation for an endothermic reaction can be written in two ways. For instance, consider the water-gas reaction for the preparation of hydrogen. The thermochemical equation may be written either

$$C(s) + H_2O(g) + \text{heat} \rightarrow CO(g) + H_2(g)$$

or

$$C(s) + H_2O(g) \rightarrow CO(g) + H_2(g) - \text{heat}$$

You can see that the heat can be transposed across the $\rightarrow$ just as if the $\rightarrow$ were an equals sign in a mathematical equation. Most thermochemical equations are written so that the heat appears on the right-hand side.

All chemical changes result in the formation of _____ _____ and a change in ____ _____.   *new substances* / *energy*

Physical changes, too, are accompanied by a change in _____, but no new substances are formed.   *energy*

Since energy (heat) is needed to melt ice, melting is an _____ergic change. It is a (chemical/physical) _____ change because no new substances are formed.   *endo* / *physical*

This equation represents a(n) _____ chemical reaction:

exothermic

$$C(s) + O_2(g) \rightarrow CO_2 + heat$$

The decomposition of solid mercuric oxide (HgO) into
mercury and oxygen is endothermic. The correct thermochemical equation is _____.

$2HgO(s) + heat \rightarrow$
$2Hg(l) + O_2(g)$
or $\quad 2HgO(s) \rightarrow$
$2Hg(l) + O_2(g)$
$- heat$

1.3   The equilibrium state

You have seen that every chemical reaction involves a change in energy, usually
in the form of heat. You also know that strongly exothermic reactions tend to occur
readily and that endothermic reactions must be carried out under special conditions. Chemical reactions go at different velocities, depending on the nature of the
reactants, their concentrations, the temperature, and the presence or absence of
a catalyst.

Despite the slowness of some reactions, you might think that all chemical
reactions through the ages should have *gone to completion* by now. That is, all possible reactants should have reacted completely to form products. Such a statement
is obviously false. The reason it is false, however, may not be so obvious.

The reason is that the products of a chemical reaction may react to yield the
original substances again. For instance, consider the reaction between hot iron
and steam

$$3Fe(s) + 4H_2O(g) \rightarrow Fe_3O_4(s) + 4H_2(g)$$

The reaction is used industrially as a source of hydrogen gas. If hydrogen gas is
passed over hot Fe_3O_4, however, the products are iron and steam

$$Fe_3O_4(s) + 4H_2(g) \rightarrow 3Fe(s) + 4H_2O(g)$$

A reaction that can proceed in either direction is called a *reversible reaction*.
Most chemical reactions are reversible to some extent. This fact is recognized by
using a double arrow $\rightleftharpoons$ in the chemical equation. Both of the reactions mentioned
above can be represented by

$$3Fe(s) + 4H_2O(g) \rightleftharpoons Fe_3O_4(s) + 4H_2(g)$$

The fact that chemical reactions are reversible leads to a situation called *chemical equilibrium*. Chemical equilibrium can best be explained by an example. Let's consider the manufacture of ammonia from hydrogen and nitrogen. The overall process is shown by the equation

$$N_2(g) + 3H_2(g) \rightleftharpoons 2NH_3(g) + \text{heat}$$

When N_2 and H_2 are mixed together, the only reaction that can take place initially is the formation of NH_3. As soon as some NH_3 is formed, it begins to decompose into H_2 and N_2. At first, the NH_3 decomposes slowly since there is very little present (a low concentration). As time goes by and the N_2 and H_2 are used up, they will react less rapidly because their concentrations have been decreasing. At the same time the NH_3 decomposes more rapidly because its concentration has been increasing. Eventually there will be a time when the forward (formation) reaction will have exactly the same velocity as the reverse (decomposition) reaction. When the two opposite reactions have exactly the same velocity, the concentrations of N_2, H_2, and NH_3 remain constant. The system is said to have come to chemical equilibrium. Once established, this equilibrium state persists indefinitely and, unless disturbed, will last forever.

When reacting substances are brought together, the conversion of _____ to _____ is often incomplete.	*reactants; products* (in this order)
The reason for this incomplete conversion is that many chemical reactions are _____.	*reversible*
The symbol _____ is usually used to indicate that a reaction is reversible. It means that the reaction takes place in both the _____ and _____ directions at the same time.	$\rightleftharpoons$ *forward; reverse*
When a state of chemical equilibrium exists, two opposite chemical reactions are occurring at _____ _____.	*exactly the same rate*
If two opposing chemical reactions are occurring at exactly the same rate, the system is in a state of _____ _____.	*chemical equilibrium*
If a system is in chemical equilibrium, the concentrations of all substances remain _____.	*constant*

If the concentrations of substances in a chemical system do not change with the passage of time, the system is in a _____ _____.

state of chemical equilibrium

Chemical equilibrium may be defined as _____ _____.

a state in which two opposing chemical reactions are taking place at exactly the same rate.

A chemical equilibrium may be contrasted with the physical equilibrium between a liquid and its vapor. If a liquid is placed in a closed container, some of it will evaporate. Before too long, however, the space above the liquid becomes saturated with the vapor, and a state of physical equilibrium is reached. The rate of evaporation is exactly equal to the rate of condensation. Since these are physical changes, it is a physical equilibrium, not a chemical equilibrium. It is important for you to understand that a chemical equilibrium involves two opposing chemical reactions. Let's examine the reaction for the manufacture of ammonia closely. The equation is

$$N_2(g) + 3H_2(g) \rightleftharpoons 2NH_3(g) + \text{heat}$$

When this chemical system has reached equilibrium, we know that the formation and decomposition of NH_3 are proceeding at exactly the same rates and that the concentrations of all three substances remain constant.

Does the fact that the concentrations of H_2, N_2, and NH_3 remain constant prove that the opposing chemical reactions continue to take place?

If your answer is Yes   Go to A below

If your answer is No   Go to B below

A

You are incorrect. How do the unchanging concentrations prove that the reactions do not stop? Suppose there are 15 students in a classroom. Suppose further that every minute 1 student enters and another leaves so that there are always 15 in the room. After observing this situation for some time, you go for a cup of coffee. When you return a half-hour later, there are still 15 students in the room. Can you be sure that students have continued to enter and leave the room while you were gone? Of course not.

The same reasoning can be applied to chemical equilibrium. The mere fact that concentrations of reactants do not change does not prove that the opposing reactions will continue to occur. Go on to Sec. 1.4.

B

Right. The fact that the concentrations of the substances involved in a chemical equilibrium are constant does not prove that the two opposing reactions continue. As far as concentrations are concerned, the result would be the same whether or not the two reactions continued after the equilibrium concentrations were attained.

1.4 Dynamic equilibrium

An extremely important characteristic of chemical-equilibrium states is that the two opposing reactions do continue to take place after the constant concentrations have been attained. For this reason, chemical equilibrium is said to be *dynamic*. The word implies continuing change or motion. Let's design an experiment to prove that chemical equilibrium is dynamic—that the reactions continue. We'll use the same chemical system, represented by the equation

$$N_2(g) + 3H_2(g) \rightleftharpoons 2NH_3(g)$$

(The heat of reaction has been omitted because it is not pertinent to this discussion.)

Suppose that we allow the system to come to equilibrium. Then let's remove some of the H_2 and replace it with exactly the same number of molecules of the heavier isotope D_2. You will recall that D_2 has the same chemical behavior as H_2 and differs only in its mass. After a few moments we'll analyze the entire system on a mass spectrograph.

If the opposing reactions continue to occur, which of the following groups of substances would be found?

D_2, H_2, N_2, NH_3	Go to A below
D_2, H_2, HD, N_2, NH_3	Go to B below
D_2, H_2, HD, NH_3, NH_2D, NHD_2, ND_3, N_2	Go to C below

A

You are wrong. If the only substances found in the mixture were D_2, H_2, N_2, and NH_3, it would prove that the opposing reactions had stopped. Since H_2 and D_2 react identically, some of the D_2 would react with N_2 if the reaction continued, wouldn't it? Go back and choose another answer.

B

You are not right. The presence of H_2, D_2, HD, N_2, and NH_3 would not prove that the opposing reactions had continued. The only new substance is HD. It could result from a new reaction represented by the equation

$$H_2(g) + D_2(g) \rightleftharpoons 2HD(g)$$

In order to prove that the original opposing reactions represented by the equation

$$N_2(g) + 3H_2(g) \rightleftharpoons 2NH_3(g)$$

continue to take place, some of the D_2 must show up in the NH_3. Go on to C.

C

Correct. If the opposing reactions in the system continue to occur, these substances will be found: D_2, H_2, HD, NH_3, NH_2D, NHD_2, ND_3, and N_2. If the reactions had come to a stop, the D_2 would be found unchanged. The HD results from a new equilibrium represented by

$$H_2(g) + D_2(g) \rightleftharpoons 2HD(g)$$

As a matter of fact, D_2 enters into the equilibrium system so rapidly that it is essentially impossible to measure the rate. Similar proofs show the dynamic character of other chemical equilibria. If radioactive $^{131}I_2$ is injected into an equilibrium mixture of H_2, I_2, and HI, it is soon found to be present in the HI as well as the I_2. The equation for the reaction is

$$H_2 + I_2 \rightleftharpoons 2HI$$

Another important fact about equilibrium is that every chemical system has its own state of equilibrium. Not only are the concentrations of the substances constant, but there is a definite relation among them. For instance, in the decomposition of water represented by the equation

$$2H_2O(g) \rightleftharpoons 2H_2(g) + O_2(g)$$

it is found by experiment that only about 2% of the water is decomposed when equilibrium is reached at a temperature of 2000°C.

On the other hand, the decomposition of nitric oxide (NO) at the same temperature, shown by the equation

$$2NO(g) \rightleftharpoons N_2(g) + O_2(g)$$

comes to equilibrium only when about 98% of the NO has been decomposed. So it can be seen that not all reactions come to equilibrium at the same point. These two examples illustrate that the relative concentrations of each substance present at equilibrium can vary greatly for different systems.

If the state of equilibrium is such that most of the matter in the system is in the form of products, chemists say that it has gone to completion or that the *point of equilibrium is on the right.* On the other hand, if most of the matter remains in the form of reactants, the point of equilibrium is on the left.

In a chemical equilibrium system, two _____ reactions are taking place. *opposing*

Because the reactions continue, the equilibrium is called a(n) _____ equilibrium. *dynamic*

When a reaction goes to completion, most of the matter is in the form of _____ at equilibrium. *products*

Reactions that go to completion have a point of equilibrium on the _____. *right*

When the system represented by the equation

$$2NO(g) \rightleftharpoons N_2(g) + O_2(g)$$

comes to equilibrium at 2000°C, the point of equilibrium is _____. *on the right*

When water is boiled, no decomposition appears to take place. What can you say about the equilibrium state? _____.

If the decomposition is represented by the equation $2H_2O(g) \rightleftharpoons 2H_2(g) + O_2(g)$ the point of equilibrium at 100°C lies far to the left. The reaction definitely does not go toward completion.

The decomposition of marble (a form of $CaCO_3$) may be shown as

$$CaCO_3(s) \rightleftharpoons CaO(s) + CO_2(g)$$

Where is the point of equilibrium at ordinary temperatures? Explain your answer. _____ _____.

The point of equilibrium must lie very far to the left. If it did not, marble would be useless as a building material.

1.5 Chemical equilibrium and reaction velocity

Before we go to the quantitative aspects of the equilibrium state, there is a final point that should be thoroughly understood. You know that chemical equilibrium is a state in which two opposing chemical reactions are occurring with exactly the same velocity. It is tempting to conclude that the point of equilibrium will be to the right for fast reactions and to the left for slow reactions. This is not necessarily true. *There is no direct relationship between reaction rate (or velocity) and point of equilibrium.* You can prove this to yourself if you think about the oxidation of steel wool. The reaction is the same and comes to the same point of equilibrium whether it rusts slowly or is burned rapidly in pure oxygen.

The relationship between equilibrium and reaction rate is much the same as the one between your destination on a trip and the means of transportation you use. The point of equilibrium is set by the kinds and amounts of reactants, just as your destination is set by your needs and desires. The reaction velocity depends on other factors, such as temperature and presence of a catalyst, just as your choice of transportation may be determined by the time and money at your disposal.

Another example of the independence of the point of equilibrium from reaction rate can be found in the reaction of hydrogen and oxygen to form water. The equation for the reaction is

$$2H_2(g) + O_2(g) \rightleftharpoons 2H_2O(l \text{ or } g)$$

At room temperature the point of equilibrium is very far to the right, and yet the reaction rate is so small that many years are needed for equilibrium to be reached. At 2000°C the point of equilibrium is nearly as far to the right, but the reaction rate is so great that equilibrium is reached almost instantly.

To repeat this important fact: The point of equilibrium is inherent in the reaction. The reaction rate is only an indication of the length of time required to reach the point of equilibrium.

Consider these two observations: When hydrogen and chlorine are mixed together in the dark, they react slowly to form hydrogen chloride gas. When they are mixed in sunlight, they react explosively to form the same product. The next several statements are based on these observations.

Whether it takes place in the dark or in the sunlight, the equation for the reaction is _____ _____.

$H_2(g) + Cl_2(g) \rightleftharpoons 2HCl(g)$

The system in the dark and the one in sunlight will both eventually reach a state of _____ _____.

chemical equilibrium

If all other conditions are identical, the point of equilibrium for the two systems will be _____ _____.

identical

In your own words, explain the relationship between point of equilibrium and reaction rate. _____ _____.

There is no direct relation between the point of equilibrium and the rate of reaction. The point of equilibrium depends on the reaction system. The rate of reaction is an indication of the length of time needed for equilibrium to be attained.

Although the "dark" reaction will take longer to come to equilibrium than the "sunlight" reaction, the respective concentrations of each substance in the two systems will be _____ when equilibrium is reached.

the same

Before we look at some specific examples of equilibrium systems and examine the relationships among the equilibrium concentrations of the substances, let's have a short quiz. Here is the first situation.

You are investigating the equilibrium among H_2, I_2, and HI as represented by

$$H_2(g) + I_2(g) \rightleftharpoons 2HI(g)$$

Repeated analysis of the mixture for I_2 gives these results (the brackets [ ] indicate concentration of a substance in moles per liter):

Time, min	$[I_2]$, moles/liter
0	1.00
1	0.86
2	0.43
3	0.23
4	0.22
5	0.23

1. Has the system reached a state of chemical equilibrium?

Yes   Go to A below
No   Go to B below

A

Right. Since the concentration of I_2 was essentially the same on three successive analyses, it is proper to conclude that the system has reached equilibrium. (The small variation of 0.01 mole/liter is certainly within the experimental error of analysis.) Go on to question 2.

B

Incorrect. The concentration of I_2 was essentially the same on three successive analyses. (The small variation of 0.01 mole/liter is certainly within the experimental error of analysis.) Since the concentrations of neither H_2 nor HI can change without a change in the concentration of I_2, the only conclusion is that a state of equilibrium has been attained. Go on to question 2.

2. The point of equilibrium is to the right.

Yes   Go to A below
No   Go to B below

A

You are correct. Since more than 75% of the available I_2 has reacted to form HI, the point of equilibrium is to the right. Go on to the next situation.

B

Wrong. If the equilibrium concentration of I_2 is 0.23 mole/liter, 0.77 mole (1.00 − 0.23) must have reacted to form HI. Since this is more than three-quarters of the available I_2, it is correct to say that the point of equilibrium is to the right. Go on to the next situation.

The same reaction is being studied. You do two experiments. In the first, you mix H_2 and I_2 together. In the second, you place HI in an identical vessel at the same temperature. The equation for the reaction in both systems is

$$I_2(g) + H_2(g) \rightleftharpoons 2HI(g)$$

You collect these data

Time, min	FIRST EXPERIMENT			SECOND EXPERIMENT		
	$[H_2]$	$[I_2]$	$[HI]$	$[HI]$	$[H_2]$	$[I_2]$
0	1.00	1.00	0.00	2.00	0.00	0.00
1	0.86	0.86	0.28	1.68	0.16	0.16
2	0.43	0.43	1.14		0.21	0.21
3	0.23	0.23	1.54			
4	0.22	0.22	1.56			
5	0.23	0.23	1.54			

Unfortunately, your analyst got a toothache and could not get any more data for you. Assuming that the second experiment reaches equilibrium at the same time as the first, what would you expect to find for [HI] at the end of 5 min?

0.77	Go to A below
1.26	Go to B below
1.54	Go to C below

A and B

Incorrect. Even though this is a fairly hard question, you can get the answer if you understand chemical equilibrium. You know that the point of equilibrium is determined by the nature of the reactants, their concentration, and the temperature. In this situation, the nature of the reactants and the temperature were the *same* in both experiments.

What about the concentration of the reactants? It is possible that there may be some relationship between the experiments on this score, too. In order to see it, answer these two questions for yourself, referring back to the data tabulated above.

1. If the first experiment went to completion, what would be the value of [HI]?

(*Ans.* = 2.00 moles/liter)

2. If the second experiment went to completion, what would be the values of $[H_2]$ and $[I_2]$?

(*Ans.* = 1.00 mole/liter for both)

The answers to these two questions should convince you that the two experiments involve the same total amount of reacting materials. They merely approach the same point of equilibrium from opposite sides. Go back and rework the problem.

C

Correct. The expected [HI] at the end of 5 min, when chemical equilibrium has been attained, is 1.54 moles/liter. In the first experiment you mixed 1.00 mole of H_2 and 1.00 mole of I_2. In the second you started with 2.00 moles of HI. According to the equation for the reaction

$$H_2(g) + I_2(g) \rightleftharpoons 2HI(g)$$

if the first reaction went all the way to completion, 2.00 moles of HI would be produced and there would be no H_2 or I_2 remaining. Likewise, if the 2.00 moles of HI in the second experiment decomposed completely, 1.00 mole of H_2 and 1.00 mole of I_2 would be produced. No HI would remain. The same amount of material is involved in both experiments. Since the containers are identical, you have identical systems. Therefore, it makes no difference from which side you approach equilibrium, and the state of equilibrium should be the same in both experiments. You are doing good work. Go on to the next section.

1.6 Law of mass action

Countless experiments have shown that every chemical-reaction system has its own unique equilibrium state. At equilibrium there is a definite relationship among the concentrations of the substances present. Suppose we consider a hypothetical reaction between the gases A and B to form the gases C and D. The results of a series of experiments carried out at the same temperature are tabulated here.

CONCENTRATIONS, MOLES PER LITER

Experiment	A		B		C		D	
	Init.	Equil.	Init.	Equil.	Init.	Equil.	Init.	Equil.
1	2.00	1.50	1.50	1.00	0.00	0.50	0.00	0.50
2	6.80	4.80	7.00	5.00	0.00	2.00	0.00	2.00
3	0.50	0.25	1.75	1.50	0.00	0.25	0.00	0.25
4	12.00	10.95	1.67	0.62	0.00	1.05	0.00	1.05

You should observe several things about the four experiments. The initial concentrations of A and B vary widely. At the start of each experiment, no C or D is present.

The equilibrium concentrations represent the equilibrium state of the reaction system shown by the equation

$$A(g) + B(g) \rightleftharpoons C(g) + D(g)$$

These equilibrium concentrations change from one experiment to another, but there is one mathematical relation among them that holds for all four. When the product of the equilibrium concentrations of C and D is divided by the product of the equilibrium concentrations of A and B, the number 0.167 is the result in all four. This number is called the *equilibrium constant*. It is characteristic of this particular reaction and changes only with changes in temperature. Whenever the gases A, B, C, and D exist together in a state of equilibrium, the concentrations will be such that this expression will hold true

$$\frac{[C][D]}{[A][B]} = 0.167$$

One characteristic of the state of chemical equilibrium is that the _____ of all substances present remain constant.

concentrations

Whenever A, B, C, and D are present in the state of _____, the expression $[C][D]/[A][B]$ = 0.167 is satisfied.

equilibrium

For this particular reaction, 0.167 is the _____ _____.

equilibrium constant

The numerical value of the equilibrium constant changes only with a change in the _____ of the system.

temperature

Let's look at a general equation that might represent any chemical-reaction system involving only gases. It might be

$$sA(g) + tB(g) + \cdots \rightleftharpoons vC(g) + wD(g) + \cdots$$

and means that s molecules of A react with t molecules of B to form v molecules of C and w molecules of D. The dots represent any other reactants or products that may be part of the system. The letters s, t, u, and v represent the numerical coefficients of the balanced chemical equation while A, B, C, and D represent the formulas of the reactants and products.

When the balanced equation is written in this fashion, the mathematical relation that is constant at equilibrium is

$$\frac{[C]^v[D]^w \; \cdots}{[A]^s[B]^t \; \cdots} = \text{const}$$

This fraction is called the *mass-action expression*. By agreement among chemists, the concentrations of the products appear in the numerator and the concentrations of the reactants appear in the denominator. There are four important generalizations that you must learn about mass-action expressions. They are:

1. The concentration of each product appears as a factor in the numerator of the mass-action expression.

2. The concentration of each reactant appears as a factor in the denominator of the mass-action expression.

3. The concentration of every substance is raised to the power corresponding to the coefficient of the substance in the balanced chemical equation.

4. The coefficients do not appear inside the brackets of the mass-action expression.

When a state of equilibrium is attained, the mass-action expression is numerically equal to the equilibrium constant K for the reaction in question.

The mass-action expression shows the relationship among the _____ concentrations of the reactants and products in a chemical reaction.

equilibrium

For any system at equilibrium, the concentrations of the reactants and products will be such that the mass-action expression is _____ regardless of the actual concentrations.

constant

When numerical values are substituted into the mass-action expression and it is evaluated, the result is the

_____, designated by the letter K.

equilibrium constant

The mass-action expression for the reaction

$$2O_3(g) \rightleftharpoons 3O_2(g)$$

is _____.

$$\frac{[O_2]^3}{[O_3]^2} = K$$

The mass-action expression for the reaction

$$P_4(g) + 6H_2(g) \rightleftharpoons 4PH_3(g)$$

is _____. $\dfrac{[PH_3]^4}{[P_4][H_2]^6}$

The numerical value of K, the equilibrium constant, changes when the _____ of the system is changed and is usually calculated for concentrations expressed in _____.

temperature

moles per liter

You should now be able to write the mass-action expression for any homogeneous gas reaction. Immediately you should ask "Why the restriction to homogeneous gas reactions?"

You may have noticed that all the reactions for which you have written mass-action expressions have involved only gases. Since all the gases in a mixture of gases fill their container completely, all the equilibrium systems we've considered so far have consisted of a single gaseous phase. As you know, any system of only one phase is a homogeneous system. Systems that consist of more than one phase (e.g., a solid and a gas) are called heterogeneous systems.

The concentration of any gas in a homogeneous system can be found by dividing the number of moles of the gas by the volume of the container. For example, if there are 6.0 moles of H_2 in a 4.0-liter flask, the concentration of H_2 is 1.5 moles/liter.

A 3.0-liter reaction vessel contains 5.0 moles of N_2 and 2.0 moles of O_2. $[N_2] =$ _____. $[O_2] =$ _____.

1.7
0.67

A 5.0-liter flask contains 76 g of F_2 gas. The concentration of F_2 is _____. (Formula wt of $F_2 = 38$.)

0.4 *mole/liter*

An empty 4.0-liter flask weighs 65 g. A chunk of dry ice is placed in it. After the dry ice has sublimed to gaseous CO_2, the weight of the flask is 100 g. $[CO_2] =$ _____. (Formula wt of $CO_2 = 44$.)

0.20

(If you found the last two calculations difficult, you may have forgotten that the formula weight of a substance expressed in grams is the weight of 1 mole of the substance. Thus 1.0 mole of F_2 weighs 38 g and 1.0 mole of CO_2 weighs 44 g.)

Can the concentration of solids and liquids in heterogeneous systems be calculated this easily? No. Since one of the characteristics of solids and liquids is that they tend to keep the same volume, it should be obvious that the concentration of a solid or liquid is not simply the number of moles divided by the volume of the container. Instead, it is the number of moles divided by the actual volume of the solid or liquid. Since the volume of a solid is directly proportional to the amount (weight), it can be shown that the concentration has a constant value. For example, let's consider solid CaO.

These data are pertinent: formula wt = 56; density = 2.6 g/ml.

To calculate the concentration, we can use this equation:

$$\frac{1.0 \text{ mole}}{56 \text{ g}} \times \frac{2.6 \text{ g}}{1.0 \text{ ml}} \times \frac{1,000 \text{ ml}}{1.0 \text{ liter}} = 46 \text{ moles/liter}$$

Since this calculation involved only the formula weight and density of CaO, both of which are constant, it should be clear that the concentration of CaO is always 46 moles/liter.

The formula weights and densities of solids or liquids are _____ and do not change as the amount present is increased or decreased.   *constant*

The formula weight of NaOH is 40.0 and its density is 2,130 g/liter. The concentration of solid NaOH is _____ moles/liter, regardless of the actual amount   53.2
present.

(If you had difficulty with the last two calculations, you may have forgotten that the formula weight of a substance expressed in grams is the weight of 1 mole of the substance. Thus, 1.0 mole of CaO weighs 56 g, and 1.0 mole of NaOH weighs 40.0 g.)

The fact that the concentrations of solids and liquids are constant has important consequences in heterogeneous equilibrium systems. One of the systems that you have already encountered is heterogeneous. It is the water-gas reaction:

$$C(s) + H_2O(g) \rightleftharpoons CO(g) + H_2(g)$$

According to the generalizations you've learned, the mass-action expression for the reaction would be $[CO][H_2]/[C][H_2O]$ and the equilibrium condition is

$$\frac{[CO][H_2]}{[C][H_2O]} = K$$

Remember, however, that the concentration of the solid carbon is constant. It may be combined with the equilibrium constant to give this equilibrium condition

$$\frac{[\text{CO}][\text{H}_2]}{[\text{H}_2\text{O}]} = K[\text{C}] = K'$$

In actual practice, equilibrium constants are evaluated from the simplified equilibrium conditions. Any K for this reaction which you might find in a textbook or handbook is the one indicated by K' above.

The equilibrium condition for this reaction is

$$4\text{NH}_3(g) + 3\text{O}_2(g) \rightleftharpoons 2\text{N}_2(g) + 6\text{H}_2\text{O}(l)$$

$K =$ _____ .

$$\frac{[\text{N}_2]^2}{[\text{NH}_3]^4[\text{O}_2]^3}$$

For the reaction $\text{CaCO}_3(s) \rightleftharpoons \text{CaO}(s) + \text{CO}_2(g)$, $K =$
_____ .

$$[\text{CO}_2]$$

The concentration of solids and liquids is omitted from the mass-action expressions and equilibrium conditions for heterogeneous reactions because _____ _____ .

they are constant and do not change with changes in the amount present.

1.7 The equilibrium constant

The relationship described by the mass-action expression for a reaction is called the *law of chemical equilibrium*. In a system at equilibrium, the concentrations of the substances that participate in the reaction must satisfy the condition expressed by the constancy of the mass-action expression. This is the sole restriction on the individual concentrations.

Let us now examine the equilibrium constant itself. The first thing we ought to study is the conditions under which it is constant. For any given system the equilibrium constant is independent of changes in pressure, concentrations, or the presence of a catalyst. As we have already seen, it does depend to some extent on the temperature of the system.

In the next section we shall see that a change in pressure or a change in concentration may shift the point of equilibrium in one direction or another. Even so, the concentrations of the substances that are in equilibrium will still satisfy the equilibrium-constant expression.

If a catalyst is present, the system will reach a state of equilibrium more quickly, but the catalyst does not affect the point of equilibrium. If this is true, the catalyst does not affect the equilibrium constant.

Why does the equilibrium constant depend on the temperature of the system? To arrive at a satisfactory explanation, you need to recall some of the things you've already learned.

Chemical equilibrium is a state in which two opposing reactions are occurring at _____ rates.

equal

An increase in temperature causes the rate of a reaction to _____; a decrease in temperature causes the rate to _____.

increase
decrease

If the temperature of a system in chemical equilibrium is changed, the rate of _____ _____ will change as well.

both opposing
reactions

Unless the rates of both of the opposing reactions change by exactly the same amount for a given change in temperature, the point of equilibrium will shift. Since the two reactions in question are opposites, it seems reasonable that they would not be affected to the same degree by a change in temperature. For this reason the equilibrium constant has a different numerical value for each temperature.

Equilibrium constants are determined by experimental measurements. Values of the equilibrium constant for the reaction

$$N_2O_4(g) \rightleftharpoons 2NO_2(g)$$

are illustrated by this table and Fig. 1.

Temperature, °C	K
25	0.143
35	0.318
45	0.671

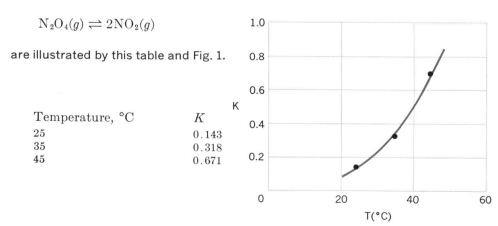

Fig. 1 Equilibrium constant K as a function of temperature T for $N_2O_4 \rightleftharpoons 2NO_2$.

Because the equilibrium constant for a reaction does depend on the temperature of the system, a careful worker always specifies the temperature at which he measured an equilibrium constant.

Equilibrium constants are used to predict whether or not a reaction will tend to go to completion and to calculate the yields of products that can be obtained.

The reaction $FeO(s) + CO(g) \rightleftharpoons Fe(s) + CO_2(g)$ goes to completion. Which of these statements is a correct conclusion? (*Hint:* Write the equilibrium constant expression for the reaction.)

K will be a very small number.	Go to A below
K will be a very large number.	Go to B below
The magnitude of K cannot be found from the information given.	Go to C below

A

_____

You are incorrect. If the reaction goes to completion, K will not be a very small number. Let's see why. The equation for the reaction is

$$FeO(s) + CO(g) \rightleftharpoons Fe(s) + CO_2(g)$$

The equilibrium condition is

$$K = \frac{[CO_2]}{[CO]}$$

The concentrations of FeO and Fe are omitted because they are constant.

The term goes to completion means that most of the reactants are used to form products. Therefore, when equilibrium is reached, most of the CO will have been used to form CO_2. K will be a large number. Go to the paragraph after C.

B

_____

Correct. Good thinking. If the reaction

$$FeO(s) + CO(g) \rightleftharpoons Fe(s) + CO_2(g)$$

goes to completion, K will be a large number. The equilibrium condition is

$$K = \frac{[CO_2]}{[CO]}$$

If the reaction goes to completion, [CO₂] is far greater than [CO] and K is a large number. Go to the paragraph after C.

C

You are wrong. It is possible to make a statement about the magnitude of the equilibrium constant. Since we're considering the equilibrium constant, the first step is to write the equilibrium-constant expression. The equation for the reaction is

$$FeO(s) + CO(g) \rightleftharpoons Fe(s) + CO_2(g)$$

and the equilibrium condition is

$$K = \frac{[CO_2]}{[CO]}$$

The concentrations of the solids FeO and Fe are omitted because they cannot change during the course of the reaction.

The phrase goes to completion means that most of the reactants are used to form products. When equilibrium is reached, [CO₂] is much greater than [CO], and K will be a large number. Go to the next paragraph.

The numerical values of equilibrium constants range from very large numbers to extremely small numbers. Every reaction has its own constant. If K is small $(K < 1)$, the numerator of the mass-action expression is smaller than the denominator. This means that the concentration of at least one of the products of the reaction is small. For example,

$$2H_2O(g) \rightleftharpoons 2H_2(g) + O_2(g) \qquad K = 4.2 \times 10^{-6} \text{ at } 2000°C$$

Not much water decomposes at this temperature and the point of equilibrium lies to the left.

On the other hand, if K is large $(K > 1)$, the numerator of the mass-action expression is larger than the denominator and the concentration of at least one of the reactants must be relatively small. For the reaction

$$2SO_2(g) + O_2(g) \rightleftharpoons 2SO_3(g)$$

the value for the equilibrium constant at 25°C is 30. This means that SO₂ is almost completely converted to SO₃ when equilibrium is reached.

In general, a large value for K indicates that a reaction
_____.

goes to completion

In general, a small K indicates that most of the material
in the reaction system is in the form of _____
_____.

reactants

Specifically, a small K means that the numerator of the
mass-action expression is _____ than the
denominator.

smaller

The equilibrium constant for any reaction can be evaluated only by experiment.
The system is allowed to reach equilibrium and the concentration of each substance
is measured. The concentrations are then substituted into the mass-action expression, and the numerical value of K is obtained. Once K has been found, it can be
used to calculate the equilibrium concentrations of the reactants and products
when the reaction takes place with different amounts or at a different pressure so
long as the temperature stays the same.

Note: Up to this point in the program, you have not been required to do much
more than simple arithmetic, which you could accomplish mentally. From here on,
the nature of the material is such that you'll have to use paper, pencil, and your
slide rule. Use care and avoid careless mistakes. If your answers aren't exactly
the same as any of the choices on a multiple-choice problem, recheck your compu-
tation first.

At some temperature above 100°C, the equilibrium concentrations for the
system represented by

$$H_2(g) + CO_2(g) \rightleftharpoons H_2O(g) + CO(g)$$

were found to be $[H_2] = 0.34$; $[CO_2] = 0.54$; $[H_2O] = 0.46$; and $[CO] = 0.65$.
Write the mass-action expression and calculate the equilibrium constant.

$K = 0.62$ Go to A below
$K = 1.6$ Go to B below
$K = 3.5$ Go to C below
Help!   Go to D below

A

You are wrong. You may have worked this problem while standing on your head. Remember that the products of the reaction are found in the numerator of the mass-action expression; the reactants are in the denominator. So, for the reaction

$$H_2(g) + CO_2(g) \rightleftharpoons H_2O(g) + CO(g)$$

the equilibrium condition is

$$K = \frac{[H_2O][CO]}{[H_2][CO_2]}$$

Go back to the statement of the problem for the concentrations and calculate K very carefully. Then choose another answer.

B

Right you are. The equilibrium constant is 1.6. Go on to the paragraph that follows D.

C

Wrong. Your choice of this answer indicates that you made a guess. Guesses will usually waste your time, so try to avoid them.

This problem must be done in two steps. The first is to write the equilibrium condition. You should recall that it involves the concentrations of all gaseous products and reactants. For the reaction

$$H_2(g) + CO_2(g) \rightleftharpoons H_2O(g) + CO(g)$$

the equilibrium condition is

$$K = \frac{[H_2O][CO]}{[H_2][CO_2]}$$

The second step is to substitute the measured concentrations into this equation and calculate K. When you have done this, go back and choose another answer.

D

So you need help. At least you're honest. The problem must be done in two parts. The first is to write the equilibrium condition. If you think you've done this correctly, the second step is to substitute the measured concentrations and solve.

If you have any doubt about your equation for the equilibrium condition, refer to C above. Otherwise, calculate K and choose another answer.

The values of many equilibrium constants for different reactions have been compiled into tables and can be found in chemistry textbooks and handbooks. In order to be sure that a state of equilibrium has been reached, a chemist makes a series of concentration measurements. When they become constant, he knows that a state of equilibrium exists.

What is the mass-action expression for the reaction $H_2(g) + I_2(g) \rightleftharpoons 2HI(g)$? _____

$$\frac{[HI]^2}{[H_2][I_2]}$$

The equilibrium condition is _____.

$$K = \frac{[HI]^2}{[H_2][I_2]}$$

At 425°C, K has a value of 54.5. In an equilibrium mixture, these concentrations were measured: $[H_2] = 3.6 \times 10^{-3}$ and $[HI] = 5.6 \times 10^{-4}$. To calculate $[I_2]$ we must first solve the equilibrium condition for $[I_2]$. Do this now. $[I_2] =$ _____.

$$\frac{[HI]^2}{K[H_2]}$$

Substitute the proper numerical values and calculate. $[I_2] =$ _____.

1.6×10^{-6}

Imagine that you are a chemist who is investigating the preparation of the gas phosphine, PH_3, from phosphorus and hydrogen. The balanced equation for the reaction is

$$P_4(g) + 6H_2(g) \rightleftharpoons 4PH_3(g)$$

When the system comes to equilibrium at 720°C in a 1.00-liter vessel, you find these amounts of substances: P_4, 1.0 mole; H_2, 2.0 moles; and PH_3, 2.0 moles. What is the equilibrium constant?

0.25   Go to A below
1.0   Go to B below
4.0   Go to C below

A
_____

Right. You can calculate K from this series of equalities:

$$K = \frac{[PH_3]^4}{[P_4][H_2]^6} = \frac{(2.0)^4}{(1.0)(2.0)^6} = 0.25$$

Go to the paragraph after C.

B
_____

You are incorrect. It is possible that you forgot the significance of coefficients in the equilibrium condition. If the equation for the reaction is

$$P_4(g) + 6H_2(g) \rightleftharpoons 4PH_3(g)$$

then the equilibrium condition is expressed by

$$K = \frac{[PH_3]^4}{[P_4][H_2]^6}$$

You should remember that the coefficients of the reactants and products are used as exponents in the mass-action expression and equilibrium condition. Go back and try the problem again.

C
_____

Incorrect. You may have worked this problem while standing on your head. Don't forget that the concentrations of the products appear in the numerator of the equilibrium condition and the concentrations of the reactants appear in the denominator. If this is what you did, you should have no difficulty in determining the correct answer. Go back and find it.

_____

As you continue your experiments with phosphine, you find another reaction mixture in the same 1.00-liter vessel at the same temperature that is composed of 0.20 mole of P_4, 0.50 mole of H_2, and 0.30 mole of PH_3. Is the mixture at equilibrium?

Yes   Go to A below
No   Go to B below

A

You are incorrect. The mixture is not at equilibrium. Since the volume of the reaction vessel is 1.00 liter, the number of moles of each substance can be substituted directly into the equilibrium condition.

$$\frac{[PH_3]^4}{[P_4][H_2]^6} = \frac{(0.30)^4}{(0.20)(0.50)^6} = 2.6 \neq K$$

You already know that the true value for K at this temperature is 0.25. Therefore, this new mixture is not at equilibrium. Go on to the paragraph after B.

B

Correct. Good work. That was a difficult question. When the concentrations were substituted into the equilibrium condition, you found

$$\frac{[PH_3]^4}{[P_4][H_2]^6} = \frac{(0.30)^4}{(0.20)(0.50)^6} = 2.6 \neq K$$

Since the equilibrium condition is not satisfied, you properly concluded that the mixture is not at equilibrium.

If the mixture is not at equilibrium, the immediate question is "What must happen for a state of equilibrium to be attained?" We know that the concentrations of reactants and products will continue to change until the equilibrium condition is satisfied. Which of the following is a true statement?

The mixture can never attain equilibrium.	Go to A below
Some PH_3 will have to decompose in order for equilibrium to be reached.	Go to B below
More PH_3 will have to be formed in order for equilibrium to be reached.	Go to C below

A

Never is a long, long time. One of the properties of any chemical system is that it attempts to attain equilibrium. If it is a closed system, it will get there eventually. Some reach equilibrium almost instantly, while others require long periods of time. Yet the fact remains: all chemical systems attempt to reach equilibrium. Go back and look at the situation again.

B

You are correct. Some PH_3 will have to decompose in order for the system to reach equilibrium. From the last problem we know that

$$\frac{[PH_3]^4}{[P_4][H_2]^6} = 2.6 \qquad \text{and} \qquad K = 0.25$$

The equilibrium condition will be satisfied if $[PH_3]$ decreases or if $[P_4]$ and $[H_2]$ increase. All three of these changes occur if some PH_3 decomposes. Go on to the paragraph after C.

C

Incorrect. The system cannot attain equilibrium through the formation of more PH_3. The equation for the reaction is

$$P_4 + 6H_2 \rightleftharpoons 4PH_3$$

The mass-action expression is

$$\frac{[PH_3]^4}{[P_4][H_2]^6}$$

From the last problem we know that the apparent numerical value for the mass-action expression is 2.6, while the equilibrium constant K is 0.25. In order for the system to come to equilibrium, the concentrations must change so that the equilibrium condition is satisfied, or

$$\frac{[PH_3]^4}{[P_4][H_2]^6} = 0.25 = K$$

If more PH_3 is formed, its concentration will increase, and the concentrations of P_4 and H_2 will decrease. The numerical value of the mass-action expression will become even larger than 2.6. This is a move away from a state of equilibrium, not toward it.

Equilibrium will be reached through the decomposition of some PH_3 into P_4 and H_2.

More often than not, it is either inconvenient or impossible to measure the concentration of every reactant and product in a chemical system. In such situations it is usually possible to figure out the concentrations. The next problem will illustrate this point as well as serve as a review and summary of this section on the equilibrium constant.

Calculate the equilibrium constant for the decomposition of water into hydrogen and oxygen from this information. 1.00 mole of H_2O was placed in a 1.00-liter container and heated to 2000°C. When equilibrium was reached, 2.0% of the water had decomposed to form H_2 and O_2.

The balanced chemical equation for the reaction is
_____.

$$2H_2O \rightleftharpoons 2H_2 + O_2$$

At 2000°C, H_2O, H_2, and O_2 are all in the _____ state.

gaseous

The equilibrium condition is _____.

$$K = \frac{[H_2]^2[O_2]}{[H_2O]^2}$$

The unknown to be determined is _____.

K

Therefore, _____ of H_2, O_2, and H_2O must be found.

equilibrium concentrations

We know that 2.0% of the original 1.00 mole of H_2O is decomposed at equilibrium. _____ mole has decomposed and _____ mole remains as H_2O.

0.02
0.98

Since the volume of the container is 1.00 liter, $[H_2O]$ = _____.

0.98 *mole/liter*

The balanced equation for the reaction shows that _____ mole(s) of H_2 is produced for each mole of H_2O that decomposes. If 0.02 mole of H_2O has decomposed, _____ mole(s) of H_2 has been produced and $[H_2]$ = _____.

1

0.02
0.02 *mole/liter*

For each mole of H_2O that decomposes, _____ mole(s) of O_2 is produced.

0.5 or $\frac{1}{2}$

If 0.02 mole of H_2O has decomposed, _____ mole(s) of O_2 has formed and $[O_2]$ = _____ mole/liter.

0.01
0.01

When these equilibrium concentrations are substituted into the equilibrium condition, we have K = _____ _____.

$$\frac{(0.02)^2(0.01)}{(0.98)^2}$$

And thus we find $K = $ _____. 4.2×10^{-6}

This method for solving equilibrium problems can be summarized in four steps. They are:

Step 1: Write the balanced chemical equation for the reaction.
Step 2: Write the equilibrium condition.
Step 3: Identify the unknown factor in the equilibrium condition and find numerical values for all others.
Step 4: Substitute and solve for the unknown factor.

This brings our discussion of the mass-action expression, the equilibrium condition, and the equilibrium constant to an end. After a brief summary, there will be some questions and problems to test your understanding.

When a chemical-reaction system has reached equilibrium, the concentrations of the substances involved remain constant. They are related to one another by the equilibrium condition. That is, the mass-action expression must maintain a constant numerical value. For homogeneous systems the concentration of each of the products appears in the numerator of the mass-action expression, and the concentration of each reactant appears in the denominator. All concentrations are raised to a power equal to the coefficient of the substance in the balanced chemical equation. The coefficients do not appear inside the brackets in the mass-action expression. For the generalized reaction

$$a\mathrm{A}(g) + b\mathrm{B}(g) \cdots \rightleftharpoons c\mathrm{C}(g) + d\mathrm{D}(g) + \cdots$$

the equilibrium condition is

$$K = \frac{[\mathrm{C}]^c [\mathrm{D}]^d \cdots}{[\mathrm{A}]^a [\mathrm{B}]^b \cdots}$$

The mass-action expressions and equilibrium conditions for heterogeneous systems do not include the concentrations of solids or pure liquids because their concentrations do not change.

The value of the equilibrium constant for a particular reaction varies with temperature, but it is independent of changes in pressure, concentration, or the presence of a catalyst. Large values of K indicate that the point of equilibrium is to the right, but they give no information on the speed with which equilibrium will be attained. A catalyst will hasten the attainment of equilibrium but cannot change or affect the point of equilibrium.

The next three problems are stated so that you can attempt to solve them entirely on your own. The step-by-step solution for each one is included if you need help.

The chemical system represented by the equation

$$A(g) + 2B(g) + 3C(g) \rightleftharpoons 4D(g)$$

is under investigation. The reaction mixture is in a 2.00-liter flask at a constant temperature of 600°C. At equilibrium, 2.0 moles of A, 4.0 moles of B, 6.0 moles of C, and 8.0 moles of D are present. What is the value of K? _____

2.4

The balanced equation for the reaction is _____ _____.

$A(g) + 2B(g) + 3C(g) \rightleftharpoons 4D(g)$

The equilibrium condition is _____.

$$K = \frac{[D]^4}{[A][B]^2[C]^3}$$

The unknown to be determined is _____.

K

The equilibrium concentration of A is _____ _____.

1.0 $mole/liter$

In a similar manner, [B] = _____, [C] = _____, and [D] = _____.

2.0
3.0; 4.0

Substituting these equilibrium concentrations into the equilibrium condition gives $K = $ _____ _____.

$$\frac{(4.0)^4}{(1.0)(2.0)^2(3.0)^3}$$

And, finally, $K = $ _____.

2.4

What will be the concentration of A in this same 2.0-liter flask at 600°C if [B] = 1.0, [C] = 1.0, and [D] = 1.0? _____

0.42

The balanced equation for the reaction is _____ _____.

$A(g) + 2B(g) + 3C(g) \rightleftharpoons 4D(g)$

The equilibrium condition is _____.

$$K = \frac{[D]^4}{[A][B]^2[C]^3}$$

The unknown to be determined is _____.

[A]

Solving the equilibrium condition for the unknown [A] gives _____.

$$[A] = \frac{[D]^4}{K[B]^2[C]^3}$$

Substitution of the known concentrations and K into the equation gives _____.

$$[A]$$
$$= \frac{(1.0)^4}{(2.4)(1.0)^2(1.0)^3}$$

From this we find [A] = _____.

0.42

Now for the last problem. Think it through very carefully. Use your head and don't make any foolish mistakes.

Hydrogen iodide decomposes into hydrogen and iodine according to this equation

$$2HI(g) \rightleftharpoons H_2(g) + I_2(g)$$

At equilibrium at a given temperature, 20% of an original 1.0 mole of HI placed in a 3.0-liter vessel is decomposed. The *number of moles* of H_2 present at equilibrium is _____.

0.10

The balanced equation for the reaction is _____ _____.

$2HI(g) \rightleftharpoons H_2(g)$
$+ I_2(g)$

The unknown to be determined is _____ _____.

the number of moles of H_2 present at equilibrium

Initially, the number of moles of H_2 present is _____ _____.

zero (none)

All the H_2 present at equilibrium is produced by _____ _____.

the decomposition of HI

From the equation we can determine that _____ mole(s) of H_2 is produced by the decomposition of 1 mole of HI.

0.50

The problem states that 20% of the HI decomposes. 20% of 1.0 mole is _____.

0.20 *mole*

When 0.20 mole of HI decomposes, _____ mole(s) of H_2 is (are) produced, and this is the number of moles of H_2 present at equilibrium.

0.10

1.8 Le Châtelier's principle

You have learned that all chemical systems eventually come to a state of equilibrium. At equilibrium, the concentrations of the substances in the system are constant and related to one another by the equilibrium-condition equation. It would appear that the yield of products in any reaction is foreordained. The only chemicals that could be produced economically in large quantities would be those for which the necessary reaction had a large equilibrium constant.

Fortunately, industrial chemists have been able to overcome this severe limitation. For instance, the reduction of iron sulfide, represented by this equation

$$FeS(s) + O_2(g) \rightleftharpoons Fe(s) + SO_2(g)$$

has a very small equilibrium constant. The point of equilibrium is far to the left. Very little of the desired product Fe is present in the equilibrium mixture. Because the reaction is used in industry, the obvious inference is that there must be a way to make the reaction go further toward completion. The first step in discovering how this is done is for you to write the equilibrium condition.

The equilibrium condition for the reduction of FeS is
$K =$ _____.

$\dfrac{[SO_2]}{[O_2]}$

[Fe] and [FeS] do not appear in the equilibrium condition because _____ _____.

they are constant and cannot change

If K, the equilibrium constant, is a small number, the point of equilibrium is _____ and the ratio $[SO_2]/[O_2]$ is (large/small) _____.

far to the left
small

As long as the system remains in a state of equilibrium, the ratio $[SO_2]/[O_2]$ (will/will not) _____ change.

Clearly, if we are to achieve our goal of shifting the point of equilibrium to the right in order to produce a better yield of Fe—and, at the same time, SO_2—the equilibrium must be disturbed. Can you see how it might be done?

If some of the SO_2 were removed from the system, the ratio $[SO_2]/[O_2]$ would decrease, and the equilibrium condition would no longer be satisfied. In order for equilibrium to be regained, additional SO_2 must be produced, or else O_2 must be used up. Both of these occur as the point of equilibrium shifts to the right. Equilibrium will be regained after some O_2 has been used up and more SO_2 has been produced. More Fe is produced right along with the SO_2.

We have found one means of displacing the point of equilibrium toward the right: *decrease the concentration of a product.*

When it is not convenient to remove the products of a reaction as they are formed, the same effect can be achieved by adding more of one of the reactants. Addition of O_2 to this system shifts the point of equilibrium to the right.

The point of equilibrium can be shifted to the right by increasing the concentration of a reactant or decreasing the concentration of a product. The converse is also true. The point of equilibrium can be shifted to the left by decreasing the concentration of a reactant or increasing the concentration of a product.

The equilibrium condition for the system represented by the equation

$$FeS(s) + O_2(g) \rightleftharpoons Fe(s) + SO_2(g)$$

is $K = [SO_2]/[O_2]$. The addition of _____ to the system will cause the point of equilibrium to move to the right.

O_2

Addition of SO_2 to the system will cause the point of equilibrium to move to the _____.

left

Addition of _____ will have no effect on the point of equilibrium.

Fe *or* FeS

Removal of _____ will have no effect on the point of equilibrium, provided that it is (they are) not removed entirely.

Fe *or* FeS

If either Fe or FeS is completely removed from the system, the equation _____ no longer represents the chemical system.

$$FeS(s) + O_2(g) \rightleftharpoons FeS(s) + SO_2(g)$$

The statement, "The point of equilibrium can be shifted to the right by adding a reactant or removing a product," is not entirely true. Why not? _____
_____.

Only those reactants and products that appear in the equilibrium-condition equation will affect the point of equilibrium. For example, in the system we've been discussing, addition of FeS *will not affect the point of equilibrium.*

In many industrial processes the point of equilibrium is shifted constantly, and the system never reaches equilibrium. When FeS is smelted, the product SO_2 is continually removed while FeS and O_2 are continually added. The result is that Fe and SO_2 are produced all the time as the system attempts to reach a state of equilibrium.

There are other ways of displacing the point of equilibrium. The displacement of chemical equilibrium is governed by laws that are included in "Le Châtelier's Principle," first published in 1884. Le Châtelier wrote, "If a stress is applied to a system at equilibrium, then the system readjusts, if possible, to reduce the stress." As used here, the word *stress* means a change in conditions. Reducing the stress means to attempt to restore the original conditions.

We have already examined the effect of the stress caused by adding or removing reactants and products. Other conditions that subject the system to stress when they are changed are temperature and pressure. The effect of changing temperature or pressure can be found in the same way that we found the effect of changing concentrations by adding or removing material. Let's consider the reaction

$$3Fe(s) + 4H_2O(g) \rightleftharpoons Fe_3O_4(s) + 4H_2(g) + 36 \text{ kcal}$$

Note: Here, for the first time, the heat of reaction is specified exactly. When 3 moles of Fe reacts completely to form Fe_3O_4, 36 kcal of heat is evolved.

This reaction is used industrially to produce hydrogen by passing steam over hot iron.

Since hydrogen is the product of economic importance, the objective is to keep the reaction going to the right. Which of the following operations will do it best?

Keep the system closed and add some steam.	Go to A below
Keep the system closed and add H_2 from the outside.	Go to B below
Remove H_2 as rapidly as it is formed and add steam as it is used up.	Go to C below
Remove both the Fe_3O_4 and H_2 as they are formed.	Go to D below

A

You are incorrect. Adding steam does increase the concentration of one of the gaseous reactants and will cause a temporary shift to the right. Equilibrium will soon be regained, however, and the production of H_2 will cease. If your process is going to make money for you, you've got to keep it going. What is another way to shift the point of equilibrium to the right? Think about it for a moment and go back to choose another answer.

B

Wrong. Adding H_2 from an outside source to the equilibrium system represented by the equation

$$3Fe(s) + 4H_2O(g) \rightleftharpoons Fe_3O_4(s) + 4H_2(g) + 36 \text{ kcal}$$

will *not* shift the point of equilibrium to the right. In fact, an increase in the concentration of a product moves the point of equilibrium to the left.

You have learned that *removing* a product will cause the point of equilibrium to move to the right. Choose another answer.

C

Correct. In order to keep the reaction

$$3Fe(s) + 4H_2O(g) \rightleftharpoons Fe_3O_4(s) + 4H_2(g) + 36 \text{ kcal}$$

moving to the right, H_2 should be removed and steam added. This is accomplished industrially by pumping steam over hot iron in the reaction chamber. This keeps the steam concentration high and sweeps the H_2 out into suitable containers. The reaction continues toward the right in an attempt to reach equilibrium. It attempts to reduce the stress caused by the decrease in H_2 concentration and the increase in steam concentration. Go to the paragraph after D below.

D

You are incorrect. Removal of both Fe_3O_4 and H_2 from the system will cause the point of equilibrium to move to the right. So far, so good. But can you fly an airplane forever without refueling? Of course not. Neither can you expect to carry out a chemical process without adding reactants from time to time. Unless some steam is added to the system occasionally, the production of H_2 will stop eventually. Go to C above.

Now that you've reviewed the effect of removing products and adding reactants on an equilibrium system, let's study the effect of a change in pressure. To determine the effect, we must write the equilibrium condition. The equation for the reaction is

$$3Fe(s) + 4H_2O(g) \rightleftharpoons Fe_3O_4(s) + 4H_2(g) + 36 \text{ kcal}$$

and the equilibrium condition is

$$K = \frac{[H_2]^4}{[H_2O]^4}$$

Suppose that the system is in equilibrium in a closed vessel. One way to increase the pressure is to decrease the volume of the vessel. According to Boyle's law, halving the volume will double the total pressure. Since solids are incompressible, their concentrations will not change and may still be omitted from the equilibrium condition. The concentrations of the gases H_2 and H_2O will double when the volume is halved. If the new concentrations are substituted into the equilibrium condition, it remains constant. (If you need to prove this to yourself, evaluate K for any arbitrary concentrations. Double them, and evaluate K again.)

We can conclude that changing the pressure does not affect the point of equilibrium of this system.

We might generalize from this single example to state that the stress of changing pressure does not affect chemical equilibria, but we'd be wrong! Let's consider one more reaction.

One of the steps in the manufacture of sulfuric acid involves the oxidation of sulfur dioxide to sulfur trioxide according to the equation

$$2SO_2(g) + O_2(g) \rightleftharpoons 2SO_3(g) + 44 \text{ kcal}$$

Suppose we have this system at equilibrium in a 1.0-liter flask. Analysis shows these amounts of substances to be present: SO_3, 0.6 mole; SO_2, 0.2 mole; O_2, 0.3 mole. What is the equilibrium constant? The equilibrium condition is $K =$ _____ .

$$\frac{[SO_3]^2}{[SO_2]^2[O_2]}$$

Since the volume of the flask is 1.0 liter, $[SO_3] =$ _____ , $[SO_2] =$ _____ , and $[O_2] =$ _____ .

0.6;
0.2; 0.3

Substituting the concentrations into the equilibrium condition gives $K = (0.6)^2/(0.2)^2(0.3) =$ _____ .

30

When the system is at a state of equilibrium, the concentrations of the gases satisfy the equilibrium condition with $K = 30$. Now suppose that the volume of the flask is increased to 2.0 liters. The temperature remains the same. The concentration of each gas is halved since there is now twice the volume to contain the same number of moles.

Which of these statements best describes the situation?

The equilibrium constant has become $K = 60$.   Go to A below

The system is no longer in a state of equilibrium.   Go to B below

The system is still in equilibrium. It has been proved that a change in pressure does not affect chemical equilibria.   Go to C below

I am utterly confused by all this.   Go to D below

A

_____

You are wrong. The equilibrium constant for any reaction changes only for a change in temperature. It does not change with a change in the concentrations of reacting substances or pressure. If the system is in equilibrium, the equilibrium condition

$$K = \frac{[SO_3]^2}{[SO_2]^2[O_2]} = 30$$

must still be satisfied. Ponder this fact for a moment before you go back to choose another answer.

B

Right. Good work. When the new concentrations are substituted into the mass-action expression, the equilibrium condition is not satisfied.

$$\frac{[SO_3]^2}{[SO_2]^2[O_2]} = \frac{(0.3)^2}{(0.1)^2(0.15)} \neq 30$$

At the moment the pressure is decreased by the increase in volume, the system is not in equilibrium. Go on to the paragraph following D.

C

Incorrect. We have *not* proved that a change in pressure does not affect chemical equilibria. No such thing has ever been proved. It has been proved that a change in pressure does not affect the equilibrium constant. When this system is in equilibrium, the equilibrium condition must be obeyed.

When the new concentrations are substituted into the mass-action expression, the result is

$$\frac{[SO_3]^2}{[SO_2]^2[O_2]} = \frac{(0.3)^2}{(0.1)^2(0.15)} = 60 \neq 30$$

What does this result imply about the state of the system? Is it in equilibrium or not? When you've decided, go back and choose another answer.

D

Perhaps your confusion can be relieved through a step-by-step consideration of the problem. The balanced equation for the reaction is

$$2SO_2(g) + O_2(g) \rightleftharpoons 2SO_3(g) + 44 \text{ kcal}$$

The mass-action expression is _____. $\dfrac{[SO_3]^2}{[SO_2]^2[O_2]}$

At the moment the volume of the container is doubled, the concentrations of all three gases are _____.

halved

The concentrations at that moment are $[SO_3] = 0.3$, $[SO_2] = $ _____, and $[O_2] = $ _____.

0.1; 0.15

When these concentrations are substituted into the mass-action expression, we find $(0.30)^2/(0.1)^2(0.15) = $ _____.

60

We know, however, that the equilibrium condition for the reaction at this particular temperature is $K = $ _____.

30

Since the equilibrium condition is not satisfied, we can only conclude that _____ _____ at the moment when the pressure is decreased by an increase in volume. Go on to the next paragraph.

the system is not at equilibrium

In order for the system to regain a state of chemical equilibrium, the concentrations must adjust themselves so that the equilibrium condition is satisfied. In the present case this can be accomplished by a decrease in $[SO_3]$ or an increase in $[SO_2]$ and $[O_2]$. This is exactly what happens when the point of equilibrium of the system shifts to the left.

$$2SO_2(g) + O_2(g) \rightleftharpoons 2SO_3(g) + 44 \text{ kcal}$$

Thus a decrease in pressure shifts the point of equilibrium to the left. A similar line of reasoning will show that an increase in pressure shifts the point of equilibrium to the right.

Where do we go from here? We've looked at one reaction that is unaffected by a change in pressure and another that is affected. Is there any way to predict what will happen for any given reaction? Yes, there is. First, however, we need to review some of the properties of matter.

You should recall that the pressure in any system is caused by gas molecules. Moreover, at a given temperature and volume, the pressure is directly proportional to the total number of gas molecules present.

Now, according to Le Châtelier's principle, a system will readjust, if possible, to reduce or overcome a stress placed upon it. If the stress is a decrease in pressure, it can reduce this stress by shifting in a direction so as to form more gas molecules.

When the system represented by the equation

$$2SO_2(g) + O_2(g) \rightleftharpoons 2SO_3(g) + 44 \text{ kcal}$$

shifts to the left, three gas molecules are formed for every two that are used up. This shift increases the pressure and reduces the stress. This result coincides with our conclusion based on a consideration of the changes in concentration.

When the chemical system

$$2HI(g) \rightleftharpoons H_2(g) + I_2(g)$$

shifts in either direction, there is no change in the number of gas molecules present. It is unaffected by changes in pressure. Likewise, the system

$$3Fe(s) + 4H_2O(g) \rightleftharpoons Fe_3O_4(s) + 4H_2(g) + 36 \text{ kcal}$$

is unaffected. We've already made this prediction from a study of the concentration changes.

In summary, a change of pressure affects only those systems in which a shift in the point of equilibrium changes the number of gas molecules present. The direction of the shift will be to reduce the stress.

A change in pressure (will/will not) _____ affect this system: $N_2(g) + O_2(g) \rightleftharpoons 2NO(g)$.

will not

An increase in pressure will cause the system represented by $3O_2(g) \rightleftharpoons 2O_3(g)$ to _____.

shift right

Ammonia is synthesized from hydrogen and nitrogen by this reaction: $N_2(g) + 3H_2(g) \rightleftharpoons 2NH_3(g)$. (High/Low) _____ pressure favors the formation of NH_3.

High

The thermal decomposition of $CaCO_3(s)$ yields solid CaO and gaseous CO_2. Is the point of equilibrium affected by changes in pressure? _____

Yes

The final stress on systems at equilibrium that we'll consider is a change in temperature. The effect can best be understood by looking at the thermochemical equation. Let's look at the oxidation of SO_2 again.

$$2SO_2(g) + O_2(g) \rightleftharpoons 2SO_3(g) + 44 \text{ kcal}$$

As written here, the reaction is exothermic. The heat of reaction, 44 kcal, may be thought of as a product of the reaction. When the temperature of the system is raised, heat is being added. The point of equilibrium shifts left, just as it would if the concentration of any other product was increased. A decrease in temperature amounts to the removal of heat, and the point of equilibrium shifts right to replace the heat.

Are you ready to put Le Châtelier's principle to work? In the manufacture of sulfuric acid, SO_3 is a necessary intermediate. It is made by means of the reaction shown above. From the viewpoint of *equilibrium alone*, what conditions will be most favorable for a high yield of SO_3?

High temperature, high pressure, catalyst   Go to A below
Low temperature, high pressure, catalyst   Go to B below
High temperature, low pressure   Go to C below

A

Incorrect. High temperature, high pressure, and a catalyst are not the most favorable conditions. Here is the thermochemical equation again:

$$2SO_2(g) + O_2(g) \rightleftharpoons 2SO_3(g) + 44 \text{ kcal}$$

A high yield of SO_3 requires that the point of equilibrium be far to the right.

An increase in pressure will shift the point of equilibrium to the right since three gas molecules on the left side are used to form only two on the right side.

As it is written, the reaction is exothermic. Heat is produced along with SO_3. Carrying the reaction out at a high temperature is equivalent to adding heat. In accord with Le Châtelier's principle, the point of equilibrium will shift to the left in an attempt to use the heat.

So, your choice of conditions would work counter to one another. High pressure and low temperature are the best combination from a purely equilibrium viewpoint.

The presence of the catalyst, of course, has no effect on the point of equilibrium. Go on to the paragraph following C.

B

Right. From the viewpoint of equilibrium alone, low temperature and high pressure are most favorable for a high yield of SO_3 from the reaction

$$2SO_2(g) + O_2(g) \rightleftharpoons 2SO_3(g) + 44 \text{ kcal}$$

The presence of a catalyst has no effect on the point of equilibrium. Go on to the paragraph which follows C.

C

Incorrect. High temperature and low pressure are definitely not favorable conditions for a high yield of SO_3 from the reaction

$$2SO_2(g) + O_2(g) \rightleftharpoons 2SO_3(g) + 44 \text{ kcal}$$

A high yield of SO_3 requires that the point of equilibrium be far to the right. Let's consider pressure and temperature separately.

Low pressure shifts the equilibrium to the left because two gas molecules on the right side can form three gas molecules on the left. The increase in the number of gas molecules increases the pressure to offset the stress of low pressure. This adjustment follows Le Châtelier's principle.

As it is written here, the reaction is exothermic; heat is one of the products. Carrying out the reaction at a high temperature is equivalent to adding heat. Following Le Châtelier's principle, the point of equilibrium will shift to the left in an attempt to use up the heat. Such a shift will lower the yield of SO_3.

From the viewpoint of equilibrium alone, then, low temperature and high pressure are most favorable for a high yield of SO_3.

In actual industrial practice, both the pressure and temperature will be set by compromise. High-pressure reaction chambers are expensive; the cost is proportional to the pressure they must withstand. This places a practical limit of about 30 atmospheres on the pressure. A low temperature favors the formation of SO_3, but at temperatures below about 400°C the reaction rate is so low that the process becomes impractical.

Although it cannot change the point of equilibrium, a catalyst will increase the reaction rate and cause the state of equilibrium to be reached more quickly. Finely divided platinum or vanadium pentoxide is often used to catalyze this reaction.

The actual industrial process involves passing a mixture of carefully purified SO_2 and air over a finely divided catalyst at a temperature of 400°C and a pressure under 30 atmospheres. Under these conditions nearly all the SO_2 is converted to SO_3, which is removed from the system.

You should now be able to predict the effect of changes in concentration, pressure, and temperature on the state of equilibrium for any reaction provided that you have the thermochemical equation. You should also be able to tell whether a given system is in equilibrium and, if not, how it will shift to come to equilibrium. Let's solve an example together, and then you can try some practice problems.

The equilibrium constant for the reaction

$$N_2(g) + O_2(g) \rightleftharpoons 2NO(g) - 43.2 \text{ kcal}$$

is 6.2×10^{-4} at 2000°C. Suppose that a 1.0-liter flask contains 0.010 mole of N_2, 0.010 mole of O_2, and 0.010 mole of NO at 2000°C. Is the system in equilibrium?

Since we already have the balanced equation, our next step is to write the equilibrium condition.

$$K = 6.2 \times 10^{-4} = \frac{[NO]^2}{[N_2][O_2]}$$

Next substitute the concentrations into the mass-action expression. Since the volume of the flask is 1.0 liter, the concentrations are numerically equal to the number of moles.

$$\frac{[NO]^2}{[N_2][O_2]} = \frac{(0.010)^2}{(0.010)(0.010)} = 1 \neq K$$

The system is not at equilibrium. Since 1 is larger than K, some NO must decompose to form N_2 and O_2 in order for the system to reach equilibrium.

Your next three practice problems will all be concerned with the same reaction. Copy the thermochemical equation and the value of K on a piece of scratch paper now.

Suppose that the same 1.0-liter flask is found to contain 1.0×10^{-3} mole of N_2, 2.0×10^{-1} mole of O_2, and 3.0×10^{-4} mole of NO at 2000°C. Is the system at equilibrium? If not, which way must it shift to reach equilibrium?

Yes.   Go to A below
No, it will shift right. Go to B below
No, it will shift left.   Go to C below

A

You are wrong. The system is not at equilibrium.

The mass-action expression is _____. $\dfrac{[NO]^2}{[N_2][O_2]}$

Substituting the given concentrations and evaluating, we find

$$\frac{(3.0 \times 10^{-4})^2}{(1.0 \times 10^{-3})(2.0 \times 10^{-1})} = \underline{\hspace{5cm}} \qquad 4.5 \times 10^{-4}$$

Since $4.5 \times 10^{-4} \neq K$, the _____   *equilibrium*
is not satisfied, and the system is not in equilibrium.   *condition*

We know that $K = 6.2 \times 10^{-4}$. Since 4.5×10^{-4} is less
than 6.2×10^{-4}, the point of equilibrium must shift to
the _____ for equilibrium to be reached.   *right*

Go to the paragraph which follows C.

B

You are correct. The equilibrium condition is not satisfied. The value of the mass-action expression is less than K, so the system shifts to the right to reach equilibrium. Go to the paragraph following C.

C

You are partly right. The system is not in equilibrium, but it does not shift to the left to reach equilibrium. Using the given concentrations, the value of the mass-action expression is

$$\frac{[NO]^2}{[N_2][O_2]} = \frac{(3.0 \times 10^{-4})^2}{(1.0 \times 10^{-3})(2.0 \times 10^{-1})} = 4.5 \times 10^{-4}$$

The numerical value of K is 6.2×10^{-4}. Since 4.5×10^{-4} is less than 6.2×10^{-4}, the system must shift in the direction to make the mass-action expression increase in value. It does this by shifting right to form more NO and use up N_2 and O_2.

A 50.0-liter vessel contains 0.27 mole of N_2, 0.0062 mole of O_2, and 0.0010 mole of NO at 2000°C. Is the system in chemical equilibrium? If not, how can it achieve equilibrium?

Yes.   Go to A below
No, it must shift to the left.   Go to B below
No, it must shift to the right.   Go to C below

A

You are right. The equilibrium condition is met and the system is in equilibrium. Go to the paragraph following B and C.

B and C

Incorrect. Let's solve the problem step by step to discover your error.

The mass-action expression is _____. $\dfrac{[NO]^2}{[N_2][O_2]}$

The equilibrium condition is _____. $K = \dfrac{[NO]^2}{[N_2][O_2]}$

If 0.27 mole of N_2 is contained in a 50.0-liter flask, $[N_2] =$ _____. 5.4×10^{-3}

Similarly, $[NO] =$ _____, and $[O_2] =$ _____. 2.0×10^{-5}
1.24×10^{-4}

Substituting these values into the mass-action expression, we find its value to be _____. 6.2×10^{-4}

Since $6.2 \times 10^{-4} = K$, the system (is/is not) _____ _____ in a state of equilibrium. *is*

Go to the next paragraph.

Suppose that the mixture that is in equilibrium in the 50.0-liter flask at 2000° C is heated to 2500°C. What will happen?

The system will remain in equilibrium.	Go to A below
The reaction will shift to the left.	Go to B below
The reaction will shift to the right.	Go to C below

A

You are incorrect. You should remember that the one change that affects an equilibrium constant is a change in temperature. When a system at equilibrium is subjected to a change in temperature, the value of the equilibrium constant will change. The system must then adjust itself to the new equilibrium condition.

The direction of the shift can be predicted by applying Le Châtelier's principle. For example, consider the reaction represented by the equation

$$2SO_2(g) + O_2(g) \rightleftharpoons 2SO_3(g) + 44 \text{ kcal}$$

The reaction is exothermic; heat is one of the products. Raising the temperature of the system is equivalent to adding heat; the system reduces the stress by shifting to the left to use up some of the heat.

The thermochemical equation for the reaction you are studying is

$$N_2(g) + O_2(g) \rightleftharpoons 2NO(g) - 43.2 \text{ kcal}$$

Apply Le Châtelier's principle and turn back to choose another answer.

B

You are partly right. The point of equilibrium will shift when the temperature is raised. It will not, however, shift to the left.

The thermochemical equation for the reaction is

$$N_2(g) + O_2(g) \rightleftharpoons 2NO(g) - 43.2 \text{ kcal}$$

When the temperature is raised, the point of equilibrium will shift in the direction that will use up the added heat. In this case, to the right. Go to the paragraph which follows C.

C

You are correct. The point of equilibrium for this endothermic reaction shifts to the right to use up the heat that is added when the temperature is increased. This shift follows Le Châtelier's principle.

In this section we have discovered that it is often possible to choose the conditions for a chemical reaction in such a way that the yield of a product can be increased or decreased. The shift of the point of equilibrium is found by applying Le Châtelier's principle: "If a stress is applied to a system at equilibrium, then the system readjusts, if possible, to reduce the stress." Changes in concentration, temperature, and pressure are among the stresses that can be applied.

The point of equilibrium is affected by changes in the concentration of only those substances that appear in the equilibrium condition (mass-action expression).

A change in the pressure of the system affects the concentration of gas molecules only. The system will react in such a way as to reduce the change.

The effect of a change in temperature can be predicted by thinking of heat as one of the products or reactants in the reaction. An increase in temperature is effectively an increase in the concentration of heat, and a decrease in temperature acts as a decrease in the concentration of heat.

A catalyst does not affect the point of equilibrium. It only speeds up the reaction. The conditions chosen for industrial processes often represent a compromise among reaction rate, point of equilibrium, and equipment cost. An effective catalyst often is the difference between profit and loss.

Your final set of questions for this chapter on chemical equilibrium follow.

This test consists of four questions. Each one involves the application of Le Châtelier's principle to the reaction represented by the equation

$$PCl_5(g) \rightleftharpoons PCl_3(g) + Cl_2(g) - 22 \text{ kcal}$$

The equilibrium condition for the reaction is

$$K = \frac{[PCl_3][Cl_2]}{[PCl_5]}$$

Question 1: A reaction vessel contains PCl_5, PCl_3, and Cl_2 in equilibrium. What happens if some Cl_2 is added? (Answers follow Question 4.)

Question 2: A flask containing PCl_5, PCl_3, and Cl_2 is in a state of equilibrium. What is the effect of an increase in pressure?

Question 3: The three gases are in equilibrium in a flask. What is the effect of raising the temperature?

Question 4: How does the addition of a catalyst to the system affect the point of equilibrium?

---

1. The point of equilibrium shifts to the left. The addition of Cl_2 increases its concentration and places a stress on the system. The stress is reduced when Cl_2 and PCl_3 combine to form PCl_5, and the point of equilibrium shifts to the left.

2. The point of equilibrium shifts to the left. The only way that the stress of increased pressure can be reduced is for the system to shift in such a way that fewer gas molecules are present. The system represented by the reaction

$$PCl_5(g) \rightleftharpoons PCl_3(g) + Cl_2(g) - 22 \text{ kcal}$$

can do so by shifting the point of equilibrium to the left since two gas molecules are used to produce only one.

3. The point of equilibrium shifts to the right. As it is written, the reaction is endothermic. When the stress of increased temperature is applied, a shift to the right will use up some of the heat and reduce the stress.

4. The addition of a catalyst will not affect the point of equilibrium. If the system is already in a state of equilibrium, the addition of a catalyst has no effect at all. If it is not, the catalyst will cause it to reach equilibrium more rapidly but will not affect the point of equilibrium.

References

At the end of each chapter in this book is a list of references to other books with chapters that correspond to the three chapters in this programmed book. Obviously, the correspondence is not exact, but in many instances it is quite close. If you are using this book as a supplement to your regular chemistry textbook, you may find this information useful.

Andrews, D. H., and R. J. Kokes, "Fundamental Chemistry," 2d ed., chap. 13, pp. 353–379, Wiley, New York, 1965.

Gregg, D. C., "Principles of Chemistry," 2d ed., sec. 18.8, pp. 428–431, chap. 19, pp. 454–471, Allyn and Bacon, Boston, 1963.

Mahan, B. H., "University Chemistry," chap. 5, pp. 145–161, Addison-Wesley, Reading, Mass., 1965.

Pauling, L., "College Chemistry," 3d ed., sec. 16-2, p. 442, chap. 18, pp. 486–514, Freeman, San Francisco, 1964.

Quagliano, J. V., "Chemistry," 2d ed., chaps. 21, 22, and 23, pp. 487–560, Prentice-Hall, Englewood Cliffs, N.J., 1963.

Sienko, M. J., and R. A. Plane, "Chemistry," 3d ed., chap. 13, pp. 269–292, McGraw-Hill, New York, 1966.

Sienko, M. J., and R. A. Plane, "Chemistry: Principles and Properties," chap. 11, pp. 239–257, McGraw-Hill, New York, 1966.

Sisler, H. H., C. A. VanderWerf, and A. W. Davidson, "College Chemistry: A Systematic Approach," 2d ed., chap. 12, pp. 193–214, Macmillan, New York, 1961.

Timm, J. A., "General Chemistry," 4th ed., chap. 22, pp. 297–312, McGraw-Hill, New York, 1966.

solutions

The word *solution* is probably one you have been using for a long time. As you continue your study of chemistry, however, you will need to know its exact meaning and be able to tell whether a given sample of matter is really a solution or not. In order to help you make such a decision, we must review the subject of mixtures briefly.

2.1 Homogeneous and heterogeneous mixtures

Most natural materials are mixtures. Pure chemical substances such as the elements iron and gold or the compounds sugar and salt rarely occur in nature. In a mixture of sand and water, there are some parts which have the properties of sand and some which have the properties of water. Mixtures of this kind are called *heterogeneous*, from the Greek words for "different kind."

The mixture of sand and water consists of two phases, where the term *phase* is used to define any part of the mixture with a uniform set of properties. Sand and water form a two-phase system no matter how much water or how many grains of sand are present. All the grains of sand have the characteristic properties of sand and constitute the sand phase. Likewise, all the water is one phase with one set of properties.

Heterogeneous mixtures, then, are those in which the separate components can be seen; there are two or more phases. A raisin cookie is a heterogeneous mixture. So are soils, rocks, orange juice, and oil and vinegar salad dressing. Even a peanut butter sandwich is a heterogeneous mixture.

If we consider either the water or sand in our heterogeneous mixture separately, each has its own set of properties, which are the same throughout the phase. Each one is *homogeneous*, a word derived from the Greek words for "same kind."

Similarly, a homogeneous mixture is one which has a single phase. Tea with sugar is an example of a homogeneous mixture. Once it has been stirred, it is the same throughout. The individual components of the mixture cannot be distinguished; it consists of a single phase. Air and sea water are two more examples of homogeneous mixtures.

Elements and compounds are pure _____ and are not often found in nature.

substances

Natural materials such as wood, coal, air, and earth are

_____.

mixtures

Heterogeneous mixtures can be recognized by the presence of at least two _____, or regions of uniform properties.

phases

Suppose some solid-colored marbles are placed in a jar of water (see Fig. 2). Disregarding the jar, there is (are) _____ phase(s).

two

If a few spotted marbles are added, there are _____ phases.

three

Mixtures that appear to be the same throughout are _____ mixtures.

homogeneous

Homogeneous mixtures consist of _____ phase(s).

one

The properties of a heterogeneous mixture are merely the sum of the properties of the individual components that make up the mixture. Homogeneous mixtures have properties that may differ radically from those of the individual components. The freezing point of a solution of ethylene glycol in water is lower than that of the water alone. Syrup, a solution of sugar in water, has a viscosity much different

 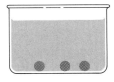 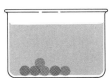

Fig. 2 Homogeneous and heterogeneous systems.

from either component alone. Tea with sugar certainly tastes different from either tea or sugar alone.

A solution may be defined as *a homogeneous mixture of two or more components*. Thus, tea with sugar, air, and sea water are all solutions. Most chemical reactions in the laboratory and industrial plants occur between solutions. Respiration, digestion, and the myriad other life processes are also reactions of solutions.

This chapter and the one following will help you to understand and learn about solutions and their properties.

All solutions are _____ mixtures. *homogeneous*

If one examines a few grains of pepper, he can readily see that pepper is a _____ mixture. *heterogeneous*

In addition to being uniform throughout, homogeneous mixtures usually have properties that are (the same as/ different from) _____ those of their *different from* components.

Oxygen, nitrogen, and the other gases are all _____ *components* _____ of the mixture we call air. It is a solution because there is only one _____ . *phase*

Ordinary milk (is/is not) _____ a solution *is not* because _____ . *it is not uniform throughout. There are two phases, milk and cream.*

When table salt is stirred into a glass of water, the mixture that results is a(n) _____ *homogeneous mix-* _____ . *ture* or *solution*

Solutions are sometimes said to be *optically homogeneous*. This means that the particles of the components of the mixture are so small that they can't be seen with the most powerful microscope. They are of molecular size and are uniformly dispersed.

Sand and water are a heterogeneous mixture because the particles are large enough to be seen. Even though very fine clay in water might appear to be homogeneous, close observation shows it to be heterogeneous for the same reason.

A mixture of sugar in water, or salt in water, is quite different. After the sugar or the salt dissolves, the individual particles are no longer visible. Unlike the sand and the clay, the sugar and salt particles do not settle out. If the container has a cover so that the water cannot evaporate, they will remain in solution indefinitely.

The molecules of sugar or the sodium and chloride ions are free to move through the water independently of one another. The particles of any dissolved substance are like the molecules of a gas in this respect. In fact, all mixtures of gases are solutions.

At this point you might very well ask the question "How does a solution differ from a chemical compound?" After all, a chemical compound is a homogeneous mixture of two elements, and it has properties unlike its components. The answer to this question is that the composition of a solution may vary, and the composition of a compound may not. You should recall the *law of definite proportions:* When two or more elements combine to form a compound, they always do so in a fixed, or definite, proportion by weight. When hydrogen and oxygen combine to form water, they always do so in the proportion of 2 parts by weight of hydrogen to 16 parts by weight of oxygen.

The composition of solutions can vary. For example, some people use one lump of sugar in their coffee, and others may use as many as three or four. Nevertheless, they all drink solutions of sugar in coffee.

Matter can be classified on the basis of composition. This chart illustrates such a classification:

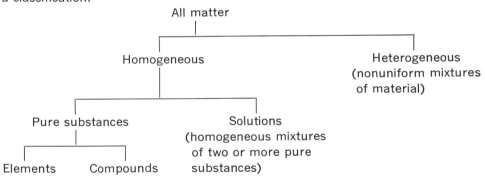

Solutions are _____ mixtures.   *homogeneous*

Solutions differ from heterogeneous mixtures primarily in the _____ of the particles which are mixed together.   *size*

The composition of _____ is governed by the law of definite proportions; the composition of _____ is not.   *compounds*

                    solutions

A solution is _____. *an optically homo-*
geneous mixture of
two or more com-
ponents

Elements and compounds are pure _____. They *substances*
are _____. *homogeneous*

Pure substances have fixed sets of properties. The properties of mixtures vary according to their _____. *composition*

2.2 Types of solutions

When you see the word solution, you probably think of a solid dissolved in a liquid.
Although this is perhaps the most common kind of solution, there are many others.
Solutions may be gases, liquids, or solids, but every one is an optically homogeneous
mixture.

Because gases have the peculiar property of complete diffusion, all mixtures
of gases are solutions. Gases also dissolve in liquids. For example, soda pop is a
solution of carbon dioxide in water, and oxygen dissolved in streams and lakes
enables fish to breathe. An instance of the solution of a gas in a solid is the apparent
solubility of hydrogen in the metal palladium.

Another common type of solution is a liquid dissolved in another liquid. Some
examples are alcohol and water, the hydrocarbons in gasoline, and automobile
antifreeze, which is a mixture of water and ethylene glycol.

Solutions of solids in solids are well known. Many alloys are solutions of two
or more metals. Bronze is a solution of copper and zinc. Not all alloys, however, are
solutions in a solid state. Some are heterogeneous mixtures of microscopic crystals
of the component metals. Others are composed of atoms of two or more metals
chemically combined. Since they are actual intermetallic compounds, these latter
alloys follow the law of definite proportions.

One of the toughest tasks that faces any beginning chemistry student in the
laboratory is to decide whether a certain mixture is a solution or not or, to put it
another way, to answer the question "Is compound X soluble in water?" Let's
devote a little time to this problem.

To begin with, remember the definition of a solution. A solution is an optically
homogeneous mixture of two or more components in only one phase. So your first
step is to look at the mixture carefully. If you can see distinctly different kinds of
solid particles or layers of liquid mixed together or if there are solid particles
suspended in a liquid, you do not have a solution.

Sometimes the solid particles suspended in a liquid cannot be seen individually, but they make their presence known by cloudiness or turbidity. This turbidity is caused by solid particles too small to be seen by the naked eye but definitely large enough to be seen under a microscope. Often they settle out if the mixture is allowed to stand undisturbed for a few minutes. Such mixtures are not solutions.

Another factor that can confuse you in your laboratory work with aqueous (water) solutions is color. Both solutions and heterogeneous mixtures can be colored. Look carefully to see if the mixture is truly transparent. Use a very strong light if necessary. True aqueous solutions are always transparent to light.

If you apply these tests carefully, you should be able to tell whether or not any mixture is a solution. (1) Are there two or more different kinds of solid particles or liquid layers? (2) If the mixture is a single liquid, is it truly transparent?

When mixed with water, the salt copper(II) sulfate gives a very dark blue transparent mixture. The mixture (is/is not) _____ a solution.	*is*
Pranksters often pour salt in a bowl of sugar. Is such a mixture a solution? _____	*No*
The salt in the sugar bowl (is/is not) _____ a homogeneous mixture.	*is not*
On close examination, the separate particles of _____ _____ and _____ can be seen with the naked eye.	*salt* *sugar*
Alloys are combinations of two or more elements that have metallic properties. They (are/are not) _____ _____ always solutions as well.	*are not*
After a pinch of solid $Ca(OH)_2$ is shaken well with a few milliliters of water, the resulting mixture contains visible particles of the white solid. $Ca(OH)_2$ (is/is not) _____ very soluble in water.	*is not*
Medicines that bear the label "Shake well before using" (are/are not) _____ solutions.	*are not*

An unopened bottle of root beer is a solution because
_____.

it is homogeneous as shown by its transparency. The label indicates that there are at least two components .

When the bottle of root beer is opened, it fizzes. It is no longer a solution because _____.
(See Fig. 3.)

two phases—liquid and gas—are now present

You have undoubtedly heard the terms *solute* and *solvent* used to designate the components of a solution. For example, in the solution of salt and water, the salt is called the solute, and the water is termed the solvent. This is a purely arbitrary designation. The general practice is to call the component that is present in the largest amount the solvent. The other components are solutes.

It should be clear, however, that there is no definite distinction between these terms after the solution is prepared. The mixture is completely homogeneous. Solute and solvent have even less meaning for solutions of gases or of liquids.

The major component of the solutions you use in the laboratory is usually water, and it is designated as the solvent. The other components, generally solids, are called the solutes. Solutions which have water as the solvent are called *aqueous* solutions, after the Latin word *aqua*, meaning "water."

You have already learned that the word *concentration* is used to describe how

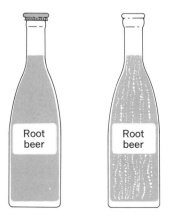

Fig. 3 A bottle of root beer, before and after opening.

much of a substance is present in a certain volume. Since many of the properties of solutions depend on the amount of solute that is present, concentration is also used to describe solutions. You are familiar with the words *dilute* and *concentrated*. They are used to indicate the amount of solute present relative to a given amount of solute.

If you dissolved a half-teaspoon of salt in a glass of water, you would call it a dilute salt solution. If you dissolved 5 teaspoons of salt, you would call it a concentrated solution.

These terms are only relative, though, and are not precise enough for most laboratory work. Over the years chemists have developed several ways of expressing the concentration of solutions. We'll study some of them in a later section of this chapter.

A solution is made by dissolving 2 g of solid NaCl in 250 g of water. The _____ is the solvent and the _____ is the solute.	*water* NaCl
If 1 g of CaCl₂ were added to the solution, the CaCl₂ would be called a _____.	*solute*
The solute with the greater concentration is _____ _____.	NaCl
A concentrated aqueous solution of sugar contains a relatively large amount of _____ and a relatively small amount of _____.	*sugar* *water*
In order to make a dilute sugar solution from the concentrated solution, _____ must be added.	*water*

2.3 Preparation of solutions

The process of solution is one in which the particles or molecules of two or more substances are separated from one another and homogeneously mixed together. Since solutions are often prepared in the laboratory, two questions are of interest: (1) How fast can a solution be made? and (2) How much of the substances can be used? Let's consider these questions one at a time. Further, let's use a solution of a solid dissolved in a liquid as a typical example.

The rate of solution depends greatly on the rate of mixing of the solute and solvent. The sugar in a cup of coffee remains as undissolved solid for a long time unless the coffee is stirred.

The rate of solution also depends on the surface area of the solute that comes in contact with the solvent. Granulated sugar dissolves more rapidly than lump sugar because it has more surface area and is closer to the final molecular size.

Most substances dissolve more rapidly when the temperature is raised. The main effect is the increased rate of mixing due to convection currents, although the rate of solution is increased to a small extent as well. (We'll see later that temperature is an important factor in determining how much of the substances can be used.) You may have observed that sugar dissolves more rapidly in hot coffee than in iced coffee.

Everyday experience indicates that the rate of _____ _____ is an important factor in how rapidly a solute dissolves.

mixing

Large crystals of copper sulfate will dissolve (faster/ slower) _____ than the same weight of small crystals in a given amount of water.

slower

Cooks often warm the water in which they plan to dissolve salt or sugar. This warming increases the _____ _____.

rate of solution

A comic sign that is often displayed on the walls of restaurants reads "Use less sugar and stir harder." Does the statement have any serious meaning? If so, what is it? _____.

The sweetness of the coffee or tea depends on the concentration of sugar in solution. Vigorous stirring will increase the rate of solution and ensure that no sugar remains undissolved

Good. The solution process can be speeded by using finely divided solutes, stirring, and warming the solution. Now let's consider the second question: How much of the substances can be used?

Suppose that you started with 100 ml of warm water and began to dissolve powdered copper sulfate (or any other soluble solid) in it. What will eventually happen if you continue to add more and more copper sulfate? You know from experience with other solutions that you will sooner or later reach a point at which additional copper sulfate will lie undissolved on the bottom of the container. This state of affairs is described by saying that copper sulfate has a definite solubility in water. There is a limit to the weight of copper sulfate that can be dissolved in a given amount of water.

If more water is added, more copper sulfate will dissolve. Even so, there will be a limit to the amount that will dissolve in the new and larger amount of water. After the limit, or solubility, is reached, no more copper sulfate will dissolve.

The solubility of $CuSO_4·5H_2O$, the usual form of copper sulfate, is 24.3 g/100 g of water at $0°C$. This means that 24.3 g of the salt can be dissolved in 100 g of water when the temperature of the water is $0°C$.

You should note carefully that nothing is said about the volume of the solution. Both the amount of solute and the amount of solvent are given in terms of weight. The total weight of the solution will be $100 + 24.3$, or 124.3 g.

How much $CuSO_4·5H_2O$ will dissolve in 200 g of water at $0°C$?

24.3 g	Go to A below
48.6 g	Go to B below
Don't know	Go to C below

A and C

Wrong. Try to visualize the situation for a moment. Think of two beakers that each contain 100 g of water. According to the information given above, 24.3 g of copper sulfate will dissolve in each one. Now pour them both into a third container (mentally, of course). What do you have? A total of 48.6 g of copper sulfate dissolved in 200 g of water. Go to the section following the solid line.

B

Correct. Each 100 g of water will dissolve 24.3 g of copper sulfate. Twice as much solvent (200 g), twice as much solute (48.6 g). Go to the section following the solid line.

The solubility of many substances in many different solvents has been measured at many temperatures. These data have been compiled and published in special books as well as in N. A. Lange (ed.), "Handbook of Chemistry," 10th ed., McGraw-Hill, New York, 1961. For convenience in comparing them, the solubilities are usually stated in the same terms. A common one is grams of solute per 100 g of solvent, just as we had above for copper sulfate. Naturally, a chemist does not always make his measurements with exactly 100 g of solvent. He measures with some other amount of solvent and calculates the weight of solute that would dissolve in 100 g of solvent.

You are a chemist who finds that 15.0 g of NaCl will dissolve in 40.0 g of H$_2$O. In your own private handbook you list the solubility as _____ g NaCl/ 100 g H$_2$O.

37.5

If you missed the last problem, do these frames. If you got it right, go on to the paragraph that follows them.

Our problem is to calculate how many grams of NaCl will dissolve in _____ g of H$_2$O.

100

From your experiment you know that _____ of NaCl will dissolve in 40.0 g of H$_2$O.

15.0

The amount of NaCl that will dissolve in 1.0 g of H$_2$O is _____ g.

$$\frac{15.0 \text{ g}}{40.0 \text{ g}} = 0.375$$

To find the amount that will dissolve in 100 g of H$_2$O, we multiply by 100 to get _____ g NaCl/100 g H$_2$O.

37.5

The two steps of this calculation can be combined in the equation _____.
15.0 g NaCl/40.0 g H$_2$O × 100 g H$_2$O
$$= 37.5 \text{ g NaCl}/100 \text{ g H}_2\text{O}$$

Another way of expressing solubility is in terms of moles of solute/100 g of solvent. For example, the solubility of NaCl calculated above is 37.5 g/100 H$_2$O at some particular temperature. We can find the number of moles of NaCl in 37.5 g by dividing this weight by the formula weight.

$$\frac{37.5 \text{ g NaCl}}{58.5 \text{ g NaCl/mole NaCl}} = 0.64 \text{ mole NaCl}$$

So the solubility of NaCl at this temperature is 0.64 mole/100 H$_2$O.
   If you understand the last calculation, skip to the paragraph following these frames. If you don't understand it, do these frames.

The amount of any substance whose weight in grams is numerically equal to its formula weight is a(n) _____ _____.

mole

The formula weight of NaCl is 58.5. A mole of NaCl weighs _____.

58.5 g

In other words, we can say that NaCl weighs 58.5 g/ _____.

mole

By inspection we can see that 37.5 g of NaCl is (more than/less than) _____ 1 mole of NaCl.

less than

To determine exactly what fraction of a mole is represented by 37.5 g, we divide this weight by the weight of 1.00 mole, or _____.

58.5 g

The calculation has this form:

No. of moles $= \dfrac{37.5 \text{ g NaCl}}{58.5 \text{ g NaCl/mole}} =$ _____

0.64 mole

How many moles of NaCl weigh 175.5 g? _____

3.00 moles

From time to time you will run across other ways of expressing the solubility of a substance. They all give the maximum amount of solute that will dissolve in a given amount of a particular solvent at a certain temperature.

A solution that has been mixed with solute until no further dissolving takes place is called a *saturated solution*. The amount of solute in a saturated solution is therefore the same as the solubility of the solute. Referring to the last calculation, we can say that a saturated solution of NaCl at a particular temperature has a concentration of 0.64 mole NaCl/100 g H_2O.

If more solute is added to a saturated solution, it does not dissolve, and a two-phase system results. The saturated solution is one phase, and the undissolved solid is the other. (See Fig. 4.)

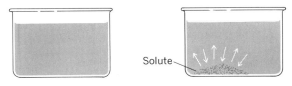

Fig. 4 Two saturated solutions.

It can be shown that any excess undissolved solute and the saturated solution are in a state of dynamic equilibrium much the same as a liquid and its vapor when they are in a closed container. In a saturated solution, particles of solute are continually going into solution, but other particles are returning to the solid solute at exactly the same rate. When this condition of equilibrium exists, the solution is saturated. A more exact definition of a saturated solution might be that it either is or could be in equilibrium with undissolved solute.

Any solution that contains less dissolved solute than a saturated solution is an *unsaturated solution*. Most of the reagents you will use in the laboratory will be unsaturated aqueous solutions.

It should be obvious that solubility depends on the nature of both the solute and solvent. Some things, such as salt and sugar, are quite soluble in water. Others, such as sulfur, are soluble to such a slight degree that they are said to be insoluble. A truly insoluble substance probably does not exist.

The degree of solubility depends on the solvent, too. Sugar is quite soluble in water, but insoluble in ether. Silver chloride is insoluble in water, but dissolves when ammonia is added.

The solubility of sucrose (table sugar) in water is 179 g/100 g at 0°C. The result is a(n) _____ solution.	*saturated*
A solution prepared from 50 g of sucrose and 50 g of water is _____.	*unsaturated*
To prepare a saturated solution of sugar in 50 g of water, one would need _____ of sugar.	*90 g*
The solubility of sucrose in alcohol is only 0.9 g/100 g. We might say that sugar is _____ in alcohol.	*insoluble*

Soluble and insoluble are relative terms just as dilute and concentrated are. Their meaning depends on the context in which they are used.

Solubility also depends on pressure, but the effect is hardly noticeable for solutes other than gases. Their solubility in liquids or solids is directly proportional to the pressure of the gas. The effervescence of soda pop, beer, and champagne is nothing more than bubbles of carbon dioxide that come out of solution when the bottle or can is opened. When the bottle or can is opened, the pressure of the carbon dioxide over the solution is decreased. The drop in pressure decreases the solubility of the gas.

The final factor on which solubility depends is temperature. With few exceptions, solids become more soluble as the temperature of the solution is raised. You may recall that an increase in temperature also increases the rate of solution. Heat is often used by someone who wants to make a solution in a hurry. He cools it before he uses it.

Sometimes, however, this procedure leads to difficulty because of a phenomenon known as *supersaturation*. "Hypo," or sodium thiosulfate, is much more soluble in hot water than in cold water. Several times more solute can be dissolved at 100°C than at room temperature. Picture, for a moment, a nearly saturated solution prepared at 100°C. As it cools to room temperature, we would expect the solute to crystallize out so that the solution would be saturated at whatever the temperature happened to be.

Oddly, our expectations are not always realized. Careful cooling in the absence of dust particles and agitation often allows the solution to reach room temperature without any crystallization. The solution is then said to be *supersaturated*. It contains more solute than a saturated solution at the same temperature.

Supersaturation is definitely not an equilibrium condition. It is a metastable state similar to supercooling. The addition of a small "seed" crystal of the solute brings it rapidly to equilibrium. The crystal grows rapidly. In a short time all the excess solute crystallizes, and the remaining solution is saturated.

Shaking the container or scratching its inside surface with a glass rod will sometimes break the supersaturation. Supersaturation is especially hard to overcome when the solute is a new substance for which no seed crystal is available. In desperation, a chemist may use dust from his pocket for seeds. Occasionally such an attempt will succeed. All that is really needed is a nucleus on which the solute can begin to crystallize. The dust may have a particle of just the right size and shape. The seeding of clouds with dry ice or silver iodide is the same sort of operation.

Let's review briefly before we go on to study some of the other ways that chemists express the concentration of solutions.

A solution consists of _____ components, but only one _____.

at least two
phase

One component of a solution is called the _____; the others are _____.

solvent
solutes

Solutions used in the general chemistry laboratory usually have water as the solvent and are called _____ solutions.

aqueous

The term _____ is used to express   *solubility*
the amount of one component that can be dissolved in
a given amount of the second to form a(n) _____   *saturated*
_____ solution.

A saturated solution and excess undissolved solute are
in _____ with each other.   *dynamic*
     equilibrium

The solubility of one substance in another depends on
_____, _____, and   *nature of the sub-*
_____.   *stances; temper-*
     ature; pressure

The effect of _____ on solubility is most   *pressure*
pronounced for solutions of gases dissolved in liquids or
solids.

The solubility of $MgSO_4$ is 26.9 g/100 g of water at 0°C.
How many grams of $MgSO_4$ will dissolve in 60 g of
water at this temperature? _____   *16.1 g*

The formula weight of $MgSO_4$ is 120. The solubility of
$MgSO_4$ in water at 0°C is _____ mole/   0.224
100 g of water.

2.4 Concentration of solutions

In your study of chemical reactions you need to know the amount of a substance
that is involved in reaction. If the reactant is part of a mixture, it is necessary to
know what proportion of the mixture that particular substance constitutes.

Since it is usually easier to measure the volume of a solution than to weigh
a solid substance, many chemical reactions are carried out in solution. Consequently, there must be exact methods for stating the concentration of a solution.
Many substances are purchased in solution. The value depends on the concentration. For example, 100 proof whiskey is more valuable than 80 proof, all other
things being equal.

2.4.1 Weight percent   One common way to express the concentration of a
solution is by weight percent. For example, if 100 g of a solution contained 26 g of
sugar, the concentration of sugar is 26% by weight. Note particularly that the
concentration is 26% of the weight of the total solution. The solution contains 26 g
of sugar and 74 g of water for a total weight of 100 g.

Let's solve one more problem together. Suppose 15 g of a solute is dissolved in 45 g of water. What is the concentration of the solute in weight percent?

The total weight of the solution is 60 g (15 g + 45 g). Of this, 15 g, or 25%, is contributed by the solute. Its concentration, therefore, is 25%.

You dissolve 18 g of NaCl in 100 g of water. What do you put on the label?

15% NaCl	Go to A below
18% NaCl	Go to B below
85% NaCl	Go to C below

A

You are right. The total weight of the solution is 118 g. The 18 g of NaCl is 15% of this total. Skip to the paragraph after C.

B

You are wrong. Perhaps you read the answers too hurriedly. In any event, let's look at the percentage for a moment.

You know that the percentage of A in a group of things containing A and B is given by the formula

$$\% \text{ A} = \frac{\text{A}}{\text{A} + \text{B}} \times 100$$

The same basic formula applies to chemical solutions. It might be modified to read

$$\% \text{ solute} = \frac{\text{wt solute}}{\text{wt solute} + \text{wt solvent}} \times 100$$

For example, what is the percentage of sugar in a solution prepared by dissolving 14 g of sugar in 56 g of water?

$$\% \text{ sugar} = \frac{14 \text{ g}}{14 \text{ g} + 56 \text{ g}} \times 100 = 20\%$$

This means that sugar contributes 20% of the weight of the entire solution. Go back and work the problem again.

C

Incorrect. Your answer is that 85% of the solution is NaCl. Is this reasonable? The solution contains 18 g of NaCl and 100 g of water. The amount of NaCl is considerably less than half, isn't it? Something must be wrong with your calculation.

To review percentage calculations, let's calculate the percentage of water in the solution. The formula is

$$\% \text{ water} = \frac{\text{wt of water}}{\text{wt of NaCl} + \text{wt of water}} \times 100$$
$$= \frac{100 \text{ g}}{18 \text{ g} + 100 \text{ g}} \times 100$$
$$= 85\%$$

If 85% of the solution is water, the remainder, or 15%, must be NaCl. If you wish, you can verify it with the formula. Then go on to the next frame.

Here are two practice frames that you can do in your head.

A solution of 30 g sugar and 60 g water is _____ % sugar.

33

To make a 25% solution from 15 g of $CaCl_2$, use _____ g of water.

45

Concentrations of solutions are sometimes expressed as percentage by volume instead of by weight. This is often done when all of the components are liquids. Wines are sometimes labeled "12% alcohol by volume." This means that each 100 ml of the wine contains 12 ml of alcohol. A 4-oz glass of such wine contains about 14 ml, or 0.24 mole, of alcohol. Beer that is "less than 3.2% alcohol by volume" does not have more than 3.2 ml of alcohol/100 ml of beer. The percentage by weight and the percentage by volume rarely have the same numerical values for a given solution.

2.4.2 Mole fraction The concentration of a solution may also be expressed as a *mole fraction*. The mole fraction of each component is the ratio of the number of moles of the component to the total number of moles of all the components. For instance, in a solution that contains 2 moles of ethanol and 3 moles of water, the mole fraction of ethanol is $\frac{2}{5}$, and the mole fraction of water is $\frac{3}{5}$.

A solution is made from 1 mole of sugar and 5 moles of water. The mole fraction of sugar is _____ and the mole fraction of water is _____.

$\frac{1}{6}$

$\frac{5}{6}$

A solution contains 1 mole of ethanol, 2 moles of acetone, and 3 moles of water. The mole fraction of ethanol is _____. The mole fraction of acetone is _____, and the mole fraction of water is _____.

$\frac{1}{6}$

$\frac{1}{3}$; $\frac{1}{2}$

From the three examples shown above, you will note that the sum of the mole fractions of all the components of a solution must always be 1.

Unfortunately, there is no convenient way to measure the number of moles of a substance directly. Instead we must weigh the substance and calculate the number of moles present.

The number of moles of any given amount of a substance can be found by dividing the weight of the material at hand by the _____ of the substance.

formula weight

If the formula weight of ethanol is 46, the number of moles in 23 g of ethanol is _____.

$\frac{1}{2}$ or 0.5

When 23 g of ethanol (formula wt = 46) is dissolved in 81 g (formula wt = 18) of water, the mole fraction of ethanol is _____ and the mole fraction of water is _____.

$\frac{1}{10}$ or 0.1

$\frac{9}{10}$ or 0.9

Suppose that 45 g of glucose (formula wt = 180) is dissolved in 250 g of water (formula wt = 18). The mole fraction of glucose is _____.

0.018

2.4.3 Molarity   For much chemical work the concentration of solutions is expressed as the number of moles of solute per liter of solution.

The *molarity* of a solution is the number of moles of solute that would be contained in 1 liter of solution. Molarity is often abbreviated as M. The unit of molarity is gram-moles per liter (g-moles/liter).

Suppose you see a reagent bottle labeled 6.0 M HNO_3. This means that the solution has the same concentration as one made from 6.0 moles of HNO_3 and enough water to yield 1 liter of solution.

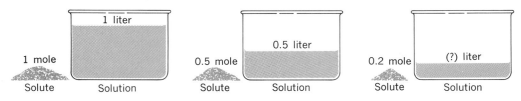

Fig. 5 Preparation of a 1 M solution.

Let's take an example. The formula weight of glucose is 180. If 180 g of glucose is dissolved in enough water to make exactly 1 liter of solution, the concentration is 1.00 M. But suppose you do not have 180 g of glucose and still want to make a 1.00 M solution. What can you do?

Remember that a 1.00 M solution is one that has the same concentration as a solution made from 1.00 mole of solute and enough water to make 1 liter of solution. Now let's suppose that you have only 36 g of glucose available. This is 0.20 mole [36 g/(180 g/mole) = 0.2]. What volume should the final solution have in order for the concentration to match the solution of 1.00 mole in 1 liter? Of course, the volume should be 0.20 liter. Figure 5 illustrates this concept.

A sample of sodium chloride (formula wt = 58.5) weighing 58.5 g is dissolved in enough water to make 0.500 liter of solution. What is the molarity of NaCl?

0.500 M Go to A below
1.00 M Go to B below
2.00 M Go to C below

A and B

Incorrect. The solution in question contains 58.5 g of NaCl in enough water to make 0.500 liter of solution. Since the formula weight of NaCl is 58.5, the solution contains 1.00 mole NaCl/0.500 liter.

The *molarity* of a solution is the number of moles of solute per liter of solution. This does not imply that there must always be exactly 1 liter of solution. There may be more or less. The molarity is the number of moles of solute that would be present in exactly 1 liter of the solution.

For instance, let's consider a solution made from 0.20 mole of solute and enough solvent to make 4.0 liters of solution. Since the solution is homogeneous, each of the 4.0 liters will contain the same amount of the solute, or 0.05 mole. Therefore, the molarity of the solution is 0.05. If you apply the same reasoning to the problem above, you should be able to select the correct answer.

c

Correct. The concentration is 2.00 M. The number of moles of NaCl that would be contained in 1 liter of solution is 2.00. It follows that the solution is 2.00 M. Continue to the next paragraph.

It is important that you remember that molarity refers to the number of moles of solute per liter of solution. This is not the same as the number of moles of solute per liter of solvent. Now solve this problem:

When 20.0 g of NaOH (formula wt = 40) is dissolved to make 2.00×10^2 ml of solution, the solution is
_____ M.   2.50

If you missed or had difficulty with the problem, do these frames. If you got it right, go on to the next section.

The formula weight of NaOH is 40. This means that
1 mole of NaOH weighs _____ g.   40

To find the number of moles in 20 g of NaOH, we divide
20 g by 40 g, the weight of _____.   1 *mole*

The operation can be expressed by the equation, num- $\dfrac{(wt\ of\ substance)}{\left(\begin{array}{c} formula\ wt\ of \\ substance \end{array}\right)}$
ber of moles = _____.

The number of moles of NaOH is _____.   0.50

The solution is made from _____ mole of NaOH in   0.50
enough water to make 2.00×10^2 ml of solution.

The number of liters equivalent to 2.00×10^2 ml is
_____.   0.200

So, 0.50 mole of NaOH is contained in each 0.20 liter
of solution. If there were a whole 1.0 liter of solution, it
would contain _____ moles of NaOH, and the molar-   2.50
ity would be _____.   2.50

The actual solution has the same concentration of NaOH. Its molarity is _____.

2.50

The last operation can be expressed by the equation Molarity = _____.

$= \dfrac{No.\ of\ moles}{No.\ of\ liters}$

What is the molarity of 750 ml of solution prepared by dissolving 0.01 lb of slaked lime, $Ca(OH)_2$ (formula wt = 74)? _____

0.08 M

If you couldn't solve the problem, or if you got the wrong answer, do as many of these frames as you need to put yourself on the right route to the correct answer.

To calculate molarity we need to know the _____ _____ of solute and the _____ _____ of solution.

$No.\ of\ moles$
$No.\ of\ liters$

We have 0.01 lb of solute. This is _____ _____ g.

$0.01\ lb \times 454\ g/lb$
$= 4.5$

The number of moles is 4.5 g divided by _____ or _____.

$74\ g/mole$
$0.061\ mole$

The volume of the solution is 750 ml, or _____ liter.

0.750

The molarity is No. of moles of solute/No. of liters of solution = _____ = _____.

$\dfrac{0.061\ mole}{0.750\ liter};\ 0.081\ M$

Frequently you will want to know the weight of solute contained in a given volume of a solution. This should be easy enough for you now.

For instance, what is the weight of $Mg(NO_3)_2$ (formula wt = 148) contained in 2 liters of 0.5 M solution? Each liter contains 0.5 mole, or 74 g, of solute. In 2 liters there is 148 g.

How many grams of CaCl₂ (formula wt = 111) are contained in 750 ml of 0.090 M solution?

7.5 g	Go to A below
10.0 g	Go to B below
13.3 g	Go to C below

A

Right. The number of grams of CaCl₂ in 1 liter of 0.090 M solution is found by multiplying the molarity by the formula weight:

$$0.90 \text{ mole/liter} \times 111 \text{ g/mole} = 10.0 \text{ g/liter}$$

The volume in question is 0.75 liter. The weight of CaCl₂, then, is found by another multiplication:

$$10.0 \text{ g/liter} \times 0.75 \text{ liter} = 7.5 \text{ g}$$

Go on to the paragraph following B and C.

B and C

Incorrect. You didn't finish the problem or perhaps your reasoning went astray. The number of grams of CaCl₂ in 1 liter of 0.090 M solution can be found by multiplying the molarity by the formula weight:

$$0.090 \text{ mole/liter} \times 111 \text{ g/mole} = 10.0 \text{ g/liter}$$

Since the volume in question is 0.75 liter, it will contain only 0.75 as much, or 7.5 g.

Notice that the unit of your original answer was grams per liter. When this is multiplied by 0.75 liter, the resulting unit is grams alone:

$$10.0 \text{ g/liter} \times 0.75 \text{ liter} = 7.5 \text{ g}$$

Go on to the following paragraph.

A variation of the same problem is to calculate how much solute must be used to prepare a certain volume of a solution with a specific concentration. For example, how much solid NaOH (formula wt = 40) is needed to prepare 4.0 liters of 0.20 M solution?

Each liter of solution will require 0.20 mole, or 8.0 g, of NaOH. There is 4.0 liters, so the total amount required is 32 g. This could be calculated from the equation

$$40 \text{ g/mole} \times 0.20 \text{ mole/liter} \times 4.0 \text{ liter} = 32.0 \text{ g}$$

Once again you can notice that the unit is proper for the unknown we were seeking. Now try one on your own.

You want to prepare 0.500 liter of 0.250 M $(NH_4)_2SO_4$. Its formula weight is 132. How much solute do you need? _____ g.

16.5

If you missed the answer, do as many of these frames as you need to get yourself on the right track.

Each liter of a 0.250 M solution contains _____ mole(s) of solute.

0.250

The formula weight of the solute, $(NH_4)_2SO_4$, is 132. The weight of 0.250 mole is _____ g.

33

Therefore, each liter of 0.250 M $(NH_4)_2SO_4$ contains 33 g of the solute. To make 0.500 liter of this solution, you need _____ of solute and enough water to bring the total volume of 0.500 liter.

16.5 g

A solution whose concentration is known with considerable precision is called a *standard solution*. Sometimes standard solutions can be made directly by weighing the solute carefully and measuring the final volume carefully. More often, however, the solution is standardized after it is prepared. You will probably work with standard solutions during your course in general chemistry. Methods for standardizing solutions will be discussed in the next chapter.

Standard solutions are often diluted in order to prepare other standard solutions. For instance, suppose you have 6.00 M H_2SO_4 and need to have 10.0 liters of 2.50 M H_2SO_4. How much of the more concentrated solution should be used?

The key to solving this kind of problem is to remember that the amount of solute in the solutions doesn't change. The final dilute solution must contain 25.0 moles of H_2SO_4 (10.0 liters $\times$ 2.50 moles/liter = 25.0 moles). The volume of

6.00 M H_2SO_4 that contains 25.0 moles of solute is 4.20 liters

$$\frac{25 \text{ moles}}{6 \text{ moles/liter}} = 4.2 \text{ liters}$$

This type of problem is known as a *dilution problem*. You'll have many opportunities to solve similar problems in your laboratory periods.

You need 50 ml of 1.0 M HCl for an experiment. The solution of HCl on your lab desk is labeled "6.0 M HCl." What do you do?

Have a chat with the instructor.	Go to A below
Dilute 8.3 ml of 6.0 M HCl to a volume of 50 ml.	Go to B below
Dilute 10.0 ml of 6.0 M HCl to a volume of 50 ml.	Go to C below

A

If you're completely at a loss, this is always a good idea. Let's see if we can help you out. You want to make 50 ml of 1.0 M HCl. Since 50 ml is 0.050 liter, the final solution will contain 0.050 mole of HCl (1.0 mole/liter × 0.050 liter = 0.050 mole).

Now your problem is simpler. What volume of 6.0 M HCl contains this same amount of solute? Let's take the number of moles and divide it by the number of moles in each liter.

$$\frac{0.050 \text{ mole}}{6.0 \text{ moles/liter}} = 0.0083 \text{ liter} = 8.3 \text{ ml}$$

And there you go! Measure out 8.3 ml of 6.0 M HCl and dilute it to a volume of 50 ml. Simple, wasn't it? Go on to the paragraph following C.

B

Right. The same amount of HCl is contained in 50 ml of 1.0 M HCl and 8.3 ml of 6.0 M HCl. Go on to the paragraph following C.

C

You are incorrect. A couple of quick mental calculations may help you to find the correct answer. How many moles of HCl are going to be in the 50 ml of 1.0 M

HCl that you need? The answer is given by

0.050 liter $\times$ 1.0 mole/liter = 0.050 mole

You propose to use 10 ml, or 0.010 liter, of 6.0 M HCl. This amount contains 0.060 mole of HCl, doesn't it? That's more than you need. If you think for a moment, you should be able to find the right amount. Then go back and choose another answer.

In all these dilution calculations so far, we've used the relationship between molarity and volume in liters to get the number of moles of solute:

moles/liter $\times$ liters = moles

Knowing that the number of moles of solute remains the same, we've used the same relationship to find the volume or concentration of the second solution. The whole process can be reduced to this equation:

$$M_1 \times V_1 = M_2 \times V_2$$

where M represents molarity, V is the volume in liters, and the subscripts 1 and 2 refer to the two different solutions. You can use this equation for any dilution problem. Want to try it out?

How many liters of 0.10 M HCl can be prepared by diluting 5.0 liters of 0.25 M HCl? _____.

$$V_2 = \frac{5.0 \times 0.25}{0.10}$$
$$= 12.5 \ liters$$

When 2 liters of 5 M NaCl is diluted to a volume of 15 liters, the concentration of the resulting solution is _____.

$$M_2 = \frac{5 \times 2}{15}$$
$$= 0.67$$

In some of the foregoing problems we've had to convert volumes in milliliters to liters and back to milliliters. For dilution problems, at least, this is unnecessary. If you look at the equation, you should see why.

$$M_1 \times V_1 = M_2 \times V_2$$

Suppose we're seeking M_2. We can rearrange the equation to

$$M_2 = M_1 \times \frac{V_1}{V_2}$$

Since the ratio of two volumes is used, it is important only to make sure that both are in the *same* unit. It can be liters, milliliters, quarts, or gallons. *Caution:* Don't get the idea that you can multiply molarity by a volume in quarts and get the number of moles of solute. It doesn't work. Look at this:

$$\frac{\text{moles}}{\text{liter}} \times \text{qt} \neq \text{moles}$$

If your lab work hasn't already convinced you of the importance of being able to work with the concentrations of solutions, it soon will. We've spent a lot of time and effort on molarity because it is the most commonly used expression of concentration. For the same reason, you ought to work the problems below before going on to another way to express concentration.

Each of these problems has been set up so that you should be able to do the computations mentally. A single equation for the solution of each one follows the problem. Don't look at it until you've worked out an answer on your own. Ready? Go.

The solute in all the solutions in these five problems is NaOH. It was chosen because its formula weight is 40, an easy-to-handle number.

What is the molarity of a solution prepared by dissolving 8 g of NaOH in enough water to make 2 liters of solution? _____ *M*   0.10

$$M = \frac{8 \ g/(40 \ g/mole)}{2 \ liters} = 0.10 \ mole/liter$$

How much solid NaOH is required to make 3 liters of a 0.25 *M* solution? _____ g   30

$$Wt \ NaOH = 0.25 \ mole/liter \times 3 \ liters \times 40 \ g/mole = 30 \ g$$

What volume of 0.40 *M* solution can be prepared from 24 g of NaOH? _____ liter(s)   1.5

$$Vol = \frac{24 \ g/(40 \ g/mole)}{0.40 \ mole/liter} = 1.5 \ liters$$

What volume of 0.08 *M* NaOH can be prepared by diluting 1.5 liters of 0.40 *M* NaOH? _____ liter(s)   7.5

$$V_2 = \frac{0.40 \ mole/liter \times 1.5 \ liters}{0.08 \ mole/liter} = 7.5 \ liters$$

What is the molarity of the solution which results when 75 ml of 0.48 M NaOH is diluted to 300 ml?
_____ M 0.12

$$M_2 = \frac{0.48 \; mole/liter \times 75 \; ml}{300 \; ml} = 0.12 \; mole/liter$$

Some chemists use an expression for concentration called *formality*. It is the number of gram-formula weights of solute per liter of solution. Since gram-formula weight and mole have been used interchangeably in this program, the molarity and formality of a solution are identical. A 1.2 M solution of NaCl is also 1.2 F

The use of molarity or formality to express the concentration of a solution has one drawback: the concentration changes with changes in temperature. A solution which has a volume of exactly 1.000 liter at 20°C may expand by as much as 6 ml when it is warmed to 35°C. A solution which is 1.000 M at 20°C contains 1.000 mole of solute per 1.006 liters of solution at 35°C, and its molarity changes from 1.000 to 0.994. Because solutions of a given molarity are so easily prepared and because they are ordinarily made and used at the same temperature, this variation of molarity with temperature is not serious (see Fig. 6.)

2.4.4 Molality If you solved that series of problems without too much trouble, you're ready to go on to the next means of stating concentration, *molality*.

Another useful way to express the concentration of a solution is to give the number of moles of solute per kilogram (1,000 g) of solvent. A solution that contains 1.00 mole of solute/kg of solvent is called a 1.00-molal solution, or is said to have a molality of 1.00. Molality is abbreviated with a small m.

A reagent bottle labeled "0.50 m" contains 0.50 mole of solute/kg of solvent. You probably won't see too many of them in the laboratory. The concentration of shelf solutions is usually given in terms of molarity.

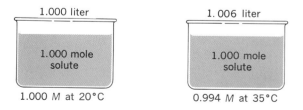

Fig. 6 Molarity changes with temperature.

The molality of a solution expresses its _____ _____ in terms of moles of solute per kilogram of solvent.

concentration

How does *molality* differ from *molarity*? Both specify the amount of solute in moles, but molality deals with the _____ of solvent, and molarity uses the total _____ of the solution.

weight
volume

It is generally easier to measure the volume of a liquid than to weigh it. For this reason, _____ is used more often than _____ to express the concentration of solutions.

molarity
molality

If a sugar solution is 0.20 *m*, the ratio of solute to solvent is 0.20 mole of sugar to _____ of water.

1 *kg* (1,000 *g*)

Right now the idea of molality may seem like just another harassment to you. In the next section, however, we'll see that the study of some of the special properties of solutions is made easier if the concentration is expressed in terms of molality.

Let's get right down to business and see if you can apply the definition of molality to a problem.

What is the molality of a solution prepared by dissolving 239 g of NaCl (formula wt = 58.5) in 2.50 kg of water?

0.995 *m*   Go to A below
1.64 *m*   Go to B below
4.08 *m*   Go to C below

A

You are incorrect. Frankly, there doesn't seem to be any way to manipulate the given data to get this answer. Were you guessing? If so, let's analyze the situation so you won't have to guess again.

The molality of a solution is the number of moles of solute dissolved per kilogram of solvent. Although the number of moles of solvent isn't given directly, we can compute it from the weight of solvent:

$$\text{No. of moles} = \frac{\text{wt of solute}}{\text{formula wt of solute}} = \frac{239 \text{ g}}{58.5 \text{ g/mole}} = 4.08$$

If all this NaCl was dissolved in 1 kg of water, the molality would be 4.08. It isn't. The total amount of solvent is 2.50 kg. The molality of the solution, then, is 4.08 moles/2.50 kg = 1.64 m.

Do you understand the idea better now? If not, go over the problem again. You'll see similar problems many times in your course. Skip to the paragraph following C.

B

Right. There is 4.08 moles of NaCl in 239 g. If the 4.08 moles is dissolved in 2.50 kg of water, the concentration is 1.64 m. Skip to the paragraph following C.

C

Incorrect. There is 4.08 moles of NaCl in 239 g. If the NaCl were all dissolved in 1 kg of water, the concentration would be 4.08 m. According to the data given in the problem, though, it's dissolved in 2.50 kg of water. This makes the concentration

$$\frac{4.08 \text{ moles}}{2.50 \text{ kg}} = 1.64 \ m$$

Continue on to the next paragraph.

If you solved that problem, you may want to skip this one. Otherwise, give it a try.

Suppose you wish to prepare a 0.20 m solution of NaOH (formula wt = 40) in 800 g of water. What weight of NaOH do you need?

6.4 g   Go to A below
8.0 g   Go to B below
10.0 g   Go to C below

A

Right. The weight of 0.20 mole of NaOH is 8.0 g. To prepare a 0.20 m solution in 0.8 kg of water, 6.4 g is needed. Skip to the paragraph after C.

B

You are incorrect. A 0.20 m solution contains 0.20 mole of solute/kg of solvent. The weight of 0.20 mole of NaOH is 8.0 g. If the problem also involved 1 kg of solvent, your answer would be right. It doesn't. The weight of solvent is 800 g or 0.8 kg. Go back and choose another answer.

C

You are wrong. By definition, a 0.20 m solution contains 0.20 mole of solute/kg of solvent. You can surely calculate the weight of 0.20 mole of NaOH to be 8.0 g. If it were to be dissolved in 1 kg of water, the entire 8.0 g would be needed to make a 0.20 m solution. According to the data given in the problem, the weight of solvent is only 0.8 kg (800 g). If the amount of solvent is less than 1 kg, won't less than the 8.0 g of NaOH be needed? If you agree, work out a new answer and turn back to see if it's one of the choices.

Like salt and pepper, molality and molarity are two entirely different things. Confusion between the two can get you into trouble. Read all the labels in the laboratory carefully.

Even when the solvent is water, which weighs 1 kg/liter, molarity and molality do not have the same numerical value.

The concentrated hydrochloric acid solution that is purchased for laboratory use contains 28.0% HCl (formula wt = 36.5) by weight. What is its molality?
_____ m.   10.7

If you failed to get the correct answer, do as many of these frames as you need to get on the right path.

When the concentration of a solution is given as 28.0 wt %, there is 28.0 g of solute/_____.   100 g of $solution$

In this particular situation, each 100 g of solution consists of _____ g of HCl and _____ g of water.

28.0; 72.0

This amounts to _____ g HCl/1 g water

$\dfrac{28.0}{72.0} = 0.389$

We seek the molality of the solution, or the number of _____ of solute per _____ of solvent.

moles; kg (1,000 g)

If the amount of HCl is 0.389 g/1 g water, there is _____ g HCl/1,000 g (1 kg) water.

389

The formula weight of HCl is 36.5. We divide 389 g by 36.5 to get the number of _____ of HCl per 1,000 g of water.

moles

The number of moles of HCl per 1,000 g of water is _____. The molality of the solution is _____.

10.7; 10.7

2.5 Properties of solutions

You are already aware that solutions have properties that are different in some respects from those of the components alone. For instance, it is common practice to sprinkle salt on icy sidewalks in the winter. This causes the ice to melt because the freezing point of the salt and water solution is lower than that of the water alone. It is also true that the boiling point of a solution is higher than that of the pure solvent. Solutions have a lower equilibrium vapor pressure than the pure solvent, and they exhibit a property called osmotic pressure.

2.5.1 Freezing-point depression   A *colligative property* of a solution is a property that depends only on the number of solute particles present and does not depend on their chemical nature. The four important colligative properties are: (1) vapor-pressure lowering; (2) freezing-point depression; (3) boiling-point elevation; and (4) osmotic pressure. Because these are colligative properties, the magnitude of the difference between the solution and the pure solution is directly proportional to the number of moles of solute dissolved in a given weight of solvent.

Freezing-point depression means that the freezing point of a solution is _____ than the freezing point of the pure solvent.

lower

Water ordinarily freezes at 0°C. Aqueous solutions freeze at temperatures _____.

below 0°C

If 15 g of a solute in 100 g of water makes a solution that freezes at −1.0°C, then 30 g of the same solute will make a solution that freezes at _____, because the amount of lowering is directly proportional to the amount of solute.

−2.0°C

Freezing-point depression is a _____ property, or one that depends on the number of solute particles in a given weight of solvent.

colligative

The molecular weight of ethyl alcohol is 46; that of table sugar is 342. A solution containing 5 g of alcohol will freeze at a (higher/lower) _____ temperature than a solution containing 5 g of sugar in the same amount of solvent.

lower

Solution A contains 5 g of alcohol in 200 g of water. Solution B contains 35 g of sugar in 200 g of water. The freezing point of solution ____ is lower because it contains the larger number of solute particles.

A

Experiment shows that the freezing point of a solution containing 1 mole of sugar in 1 kg of water is −1.86°C. The freezing point of a similar 1 m solution of alcohol in water will be _____ because 1 mole of both sugar and alcohol contains Avogadro's number of molecules.

−1.86°C *or the same*

Numerous experiments have shown that the freezing point of a 1 m aqueous solution of any nonvolatile undissociated solute is −1.86°C. In the next chapter we'll see that solutes which dissociate show a greater lowering than might be expected.

The quantity 1.86°C is called the *molal freezing-point constant* for water. It is the freezing-point lowering for a 1 m solution.

Freezing-point depression can be used to determine the concentration of a solution. Suppose that an aqueous solution has a freezing point of −0.93°C. What is its concentration? The freezing point of the solution is 0.93°C lower than the freezing point of pure water. Since a 1 m solution has a freezing point that is 1.86°C lower than pure water, the concentration of the solution can be found from the equation

$$m = \frac{0.93°}{1.86°} = 0.50$$

When 4.6 g of ethanol is dissolved in 500 g of water, the freezing point of the solution is −0.37°C. Since pure water freezes at 0°C, the freezing-point depression is _____.

0.37°C

The molal freezing-point constant for water is _____ _____. The concentration of the alcohol solution is obviously (less than/more than) _____ 1 m.

1.86°C

less than

The actual concentration of the alcohol solution is equal to the fraction _____, or _____ m.

$\frac{0.37}{1.86}$; 0.20

We have found that a solution of 4.6 g ethanol/500 g water is the same as a solution of _____ mole of ethanol/1,000 g water.

0.20

The alcohol solution we have made would contain _____ ethanol/1,000 g water.

9.2 g

This amount of ethanol (9.2 g) is 0.20 _____ of ethanol because it gives a 0.20 m solution.

mole

If 9.2 g of ethanol is 0.20 mole, then 1 mole of ethanol weighs _____.

46 g

The weight of 1 mole of a substance is also called the gram-_____ or the gram-_____ of the substance.

molecular weight; formula weight

The freezing point of a solution can be used to determine the concentration of the solution and the molecular weight of the _____ if the weights of solute and solvent are known.

solute

In actual practice, the freezing point is most often used to determine the molecular weight of a solute or as an indication of the purity of a solvent. For instance, the freezing point of pure benzene is 5.5°C. If a sample of benzene contains any dissolved impurity, the freezing point will be less than 5.5°C.

Organic chemists frequently use camphor as a solvent for molecular-weight determinations. Its normal freezing point is 178°C, and its molal freezing-point constant is 40°C. A small amount of the solute whose molecular weight is to be determined is mixed with a few grams of camphor. The mixture is melted, and its freezing point is measured. The molecular weight can be calculated from the known weight of solute, weight of camphor, molal freezing-point constant, and observed freezing point.

You want to find the molecular weight of an unknown white solid. The freezing point of a mixture of 1.0 g of the solid and 10.0 g of camphor is 156°C. What is the molecular weight?

180 g	Go to A below
55 g	Go to B below
Can't get started	Go to C below

A
_____

You are right. The molality of the solution is 0.55. If 100 g solute/1,000 g of camphor makes a solution of this concentration, 1 mole of the solute weighs 180 g. Continue to the paragraph following C.

B
_____

Incorrect. The molecular weight of the solute is not 55. Since the freezing point of the solution is 156°C, the depression is 178°C − 156°C, or 22°C. Using the molal freezing-point constant of 40°C, we find the concentration to be

$$\frac{22°C}{40°C} = 0.55$$

Now, 1 g of solute in 10 g of solvent is equivalent to 100 g in 1,000 g. So we know that 100 g of the solute is 0.55 mole. The weight of 1 mole, then, is

$$\frac{100 \text{ g}}{0.55 \text{ mole}} = 180 \frac{\text{g}}{\text{mole}}$$

Go on to the paragraph following C.

c

Let's see if we can steer you on the right track with a few easy questions.

If camphor normally melts at 178°C and the solution freezes at 156°C, the freezing-point depression is _____°C.

22

Knowing that the molal freezing-point constant of camphor is 40°C, we can calculate the concentration of the solution to be 22°C/40°C = _____ *m*.

0.55

The solution in question contains 1.0 g solute/10.0 g camphor, or _____ g solute/1,000 g.

100

Combining the last two answers, we know that 100 g of the solute is _____ mole.

0.55

Finally, then, if 100 g is 0.55 mole, the weight of 1 mole is _____ g. The molecular weight of the solute is _____.

180
180

2.5.2 Boiling-point elevation   Another of the colligative properties of solutions is boiling-point elevation. The boiling point of a solution is always higher than that of the pure solvent at the same pressure.

As you know, the boiling point of a liquid is the temperature at which its vapor pressure becomes equal to the atmospheric pressure. Because the atmospheric pressure varies, the boiling point is not a constant; it depends on the atmospheric pressure. For this reason, the term *normal boiling point* is defined as the temperature at which the vapor pressure of a liquid is exactly one atmosphere.

Figure 7 shows the relationships between vapor pressure and temperature for a pure solvent and for a solution.

At any given temperature, the vapor pressure of a solution is (higher/lower) _____ than that of the pure solvent.

lower

The vapor pressures of both the solution and the solvent _____ as the temperature increases.

increase

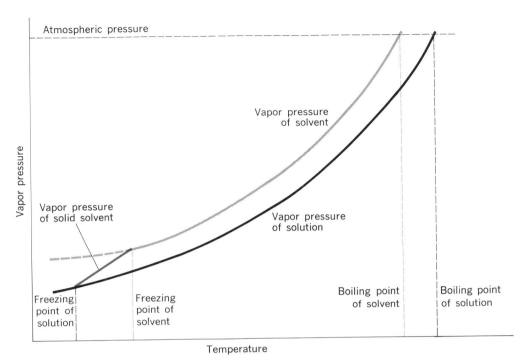

Fig. 7 Vapor pressure relationships between a solution and the pure solvent.

The temperature at which the vapor pressure of the solvent is equal to the atmospheric pressure is called _____.

the boiling point

When the vapor pressure of the solvent is equal to the atmospheric pressure, the vapor pressure of the solution is (more than/less than) _____ atmospheric pressure.

less than

Consequently, the solution is (above/below) _____ its boiling point.

below

Regardless of the actual atmospheric pressure, the boiling point of a solution is always _____ than the boiling point of the pure solvent.

higher

The effect of the solute is to extend the range of temperature over which a solution remains in the _____ state.

liquid

The molal elevation of the boiling point has a definite value just as does the molal freezing-point depression. For water the molal *boiling-point constant* is 0.52°C. This means that a 1 *m* solution of a nonvolatile, undissociated solute will boil at a temperature 0.52°C higher than pure water.

Boiling points are more difficult to measure than freezing points. For this reason, boiling-point elevation is less often used for molecular-weight determinations than freezing-point depression. When it is, the calculation is similar to that for freezing-point lowering.

The boiling point of a solution is 100.11°C on a day when the atmospheric pressure is 760 mm. The solution was prepared from 3.00 g of solute and 200.0 g of water. What is the formula weight of the solute?

14 g/mole   Go to A below
32 g/mole   Go to B below
71 g/mole   Go to C below

A and B

Incorrect. Your choice of either of these answers shows that you are probably having trouble with problem solving generally. Let's look at a similar problem.

Problem: The boiling point of an aqueous solution is found to be 100.30°C at 760 mm pressure. The solution was prepared by dissolving 5.0 g of solute in 500.0 g of water. What is the formula weight of the solute?

Although this problem may seem involved and difficult at first glance, you can solve it by a series of "thought steps," which will also increase your understanding of the principles involved in the solution of the problem. For example,

1. Since the molal boiling-point constant of water is 0.52°C, this solution must be about 0.5 *m*. (Actually, 0.30°C/0.52°C = 0.58.)

2. If 5.0 g of solute is dissolved in 500.0 g of water, this would amount to 10.0 g in 1 kg (1,000 g) of water.

3. If 10.0 g makes a solution that is about 0.5 *m*, then 20 g would make a 1 *m* solution, and the formula weight is about 20. (Actually, the formula weight is given by 10.0 g/0.58 mole = 17 g/mole.)

This "thought step" approach is a good way to attack problems that seem hard. It not only helps you to solve them but lets you estimate the magnitude of the answer. If you were merely to substitute into a formula, you might not know whether the correct answer was 17, 170, or 1700. Go back and try the other problem again.

c

Right. The formula weight is 71 g/mole. The solution is 0.212 m

$$\left(\frac{0.11°C}{0.52°C} = 0.212\right)$$

The solution contains 15 g of solute/kg of solvent. So the formula weight is 71 g/mole (15 g/0.212 mole = 71 g/mole). Continue to the next paragraph.

2.5.3 Osmotic pressure   The last of the colligative properties of solutions that we'll consider is *osmotic pressure*. Osmotic pressure results from a process called osmosis. There exist membranes called *semipermeable* because they permit the flow of solvent through their structures yet block the flow of solute particles. This flow, which distinguishes between the solvent and solute, is called osmosis. Parchment paper, cellophane, and animal membranes are semipermeable.

Although the exact theoretical explanation of osmosis is not known, there are many examples of the process. It is frequently seen in biological systems. Salts and food are transported from blood to tissue cells by osmosis. The flow of sap in plants is maintained by osmosis.

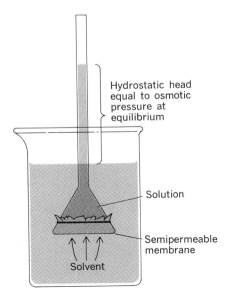

Hydrostatic head equal to osmotic pressure at equilibrium

Solution

Semipermeable membrane

Solvent

Fig. 8   Osmotic pressure.

The net effect of osmosis is to cause a transfer of solvent molecules through the pores of the semipermeable membrane. If the vapor pressures of the solvent molecules are exactly the same on both sides of the membrane, no net effect is observed. If the vapor pressures are unequal, solvent molecules will migrate from the side of high vapor pressure to the side of lower vapor pressure. This is most readily observed when the membrane separates a solution from a pure solvent as shown in Fig. 8. There is a flow of solvent from the pure solvent side to the solution side. The flow continues until hydrostatic pressure builds up to the extent that it prevents the flow. This pressure is defined as the osmotic pressure of the solution.

Since osmotic pressure is a colligative property, it may be used for molecular-weight determinations. It is used less often than either freezing-point depression or boiling-point elevation because of the difficulty of making accurate measurements of osmotic pressure.

Osmosis will cause _____ molecules to flow through a semipermeable membrane which separates solutions of unequal vapor pressure.	*solvent*
The solvent molecules flow through the membrane from the side with the (higher/lower) _____ vapor pressure to the side with the (higher/lower) _____ vapor pressure.	*higher* *lower*
This means that the solvent molecules move from the (more/less) _____ concentrated solution to the (more/less) _____ concentrated solution.	*less* *more*
If there is no way for hydrostatic pressure to build up, osmosis will continue until _____ _____.	*the concentrations on both sides of the membrane are the same*

We have now reached the end of this section on the means of expressing concentration of solutions and the properties of solutions. After a brief summary and review, we'll go on to the separation of dissolved substances.

The concentration of a solution expresses the relative amounts of _____ and _____ _____ that are present.	*solute; solvent*

The number of grams of solute in 100 g of solution expresses the concentration in _____.

weight percent

The weight percent concentration of magnesium sulfate in a solution made from 28 g of the solid salt and 172 g of water is _____.

14%

The mole fraction of any component of a solution is given by the number of _____ of the component divided by the _____ of moles of all the components of the solution.

moles
total number

The abbreviation *M* stands for molarity, or the number of moles of solute per _____.

liter of solution

1 liter of a 1.0 *M* solution contains _____ mole(s) of solute.

1.0

The amount of solute in 0.75 liter of this same solution is _____ mole(s).

0.75

The number of moles of solute can always be found by multiplying the _____ by the volume in liters.

molarity

When a solution is diluted by the addition of more solvent, the _____ changes, but the amount of solute remains the same.

concentration or *molarity (formality)*

The number of moles of solute per kilogram of solvent is the _____ of a solution.

molality

Solutions have properties that are different from those of the pure components. Colligative properties of solutions are those that depend only on the _____ of solute particles present and not on their chemical nature.

number

The range of temperature over which a solution remains in a liquid state is greater than the range for the pure solvent because of two colligative properties of the solution: _____ and _____.

boiling-point elevation; freezing-point depression

2.6 Separation of dissolved substances

One of the characteristics of a mixture is that it can be separated into its components by mechanical or physical means. A mixture of nuts and bolts can easily be sorted because of the components' different appearance. Since solutions are optically homogeneous mixtures, they cannot be separated by any method that depends on vision. Nevertheless, it is important to be able to separate solutions into their components. Many products are synthesized or purified in solution. Sooner or later the solvent has to be removed. There are several methods of doing this, and the best one for any particular situation depends on the type of solution.

If the components of a mixture of gases have appreciably different molecular weights, they can be separated by diffusion through a porous membrane. Hydrogen and carbon dioxide are often separated in this manner. Since the rates of diffusion are inversely proportional to the square root of the ratio of molecular weights, hydrogen diffuses 4.7 times $\left(\sqrt{\dfrac{44 \text{ g CO}_2/\text{mole}}{2 \text{ g H}_2/\text{mole}}} = 4.7 \right)$ faster than carbon dioxide.

Diffusion would not be a good means for the separation of O_2 and N_2 because the _____ weights of the two gases are nearly the same.	*molecular*
Hydrogen and krypton might be separated by _____ _____ because of the considerable difference in their molecular weights.	*diffusion*
The relative rates of diffusion of two gases are inversely proportional to the square root of the ratio of their molecular weights. _____ diffuses faster than _____ because of its lower molecular weight.	*Hydrogen* *krypton*
The molecular weight of hydrogen gas is 2; that of krypton is 84. Hydrogen diffuses _____ times faster than krypton.	6.5

For lack of a better method, diffusion has been used to separate the isotopes of uranium. The uranium is in the form of its hexafluoride, UF_6. The molecular weight of $^{238}UF_6$ is 352, while that of $^{235}UF_6$ is 349. The latter compound diffuses only 1.004 times faster than the former. At the Atomic Energy Commission's separation plant in Oak Ridge, Tennessee, satisfactory separation is achieved only after the gaseous mixture has been successively passed through hundreds of porous membranes.

Some gaseous solutions can be separated by means of a chemical reaction. Of course, this leaves one of the gases in the form of a compound. Oxygen and nitrogen are separated by passing the solution over hot copper. The oxygen reacts with the copper to form copper(II) oxide.

$$2Cu + O_2 \rightarrow 2CuO$$

The nitrogen passes over the copper unchanged. The respiration of animals is a similar process. Oxygen from the air combines with hemoglobin in the blood and is transported to the tissues. The other gases in the air, principally nitrogen, do not react and are exhaled together with the waste products carbon dioxide and water vapor.

Suppose that you have a mixture of nitrogen and carbon dioxide which you wish to separate. Because of the similarity of their _____, diffusion is probably not a good method for the separation.

molecular weights

If a _____ reaction is to be used for the separation, it will probably involve the carbon dioxide because nitrogen is relatively unreactive.

chemical

Carbon dioxide is an oxide of a (metal/nonmetal) _____.

nonmetal

Oxides of nonmetals are acidic; they react with _____ _____.

bases

Potassium hydroxide is a(n) (acid/base) _____.

base

When a mixture of CO_2 and N_2 is passed through a dilute solution of KOH, the _____ reacts, and the _____ passes through unchanged.

CO_2
N_2

The equation for the reaction is

$$CO_2 + OH^- \rightleftharpoons HCO_3^-$$

If desired, the CO_2 can be recovered by adding a strong acid to the solution

$$H^+ + HCO_3^- \rightarrow H_2O + CO_2$$

In some special cases, gases are separated by the adsorption of one on the surface of a solid. Gas masks operate on this principle. The poisoned air is drawn through a canister of finely divided charcoal. The noxious gases are adsorbed, and the pure air passes through.

Diffusion, chemical reaction, and adsorption are all methods that can be used for the separation of the components of a gaseous solution. The nature of each situation dictates the method of choice.

Solutions of gases in liquids can often be separated into their components by boiling them. The solubility of gases in water usually decreases as the temperature is raised. Air can be completely removed from water by boiling the water for a few moments. The flat taste of freshly boiled water is caused by the absence of dissolved air.

Some gases, such as ammonia, hydrogen chloride, and hydrogen sulfide, react with water when they dissolve in it. They can be recovered by means of chemical reactions. For example, addition of a strong base will eliminate the weak base ammonia from an aqueous solution.

Gases can also be separated from liquids by reducing the pressure of the gas above the liquid. This process is in agreement with *Henry's law*, which states that the *weight of a gas that will dissolve in a liquid is directly proportional to the pressure of the gas above the liquid.*

Carbonated beverages are prepared by bottling them with a very high pressure of CO_2 above the liquid. This high pressure causes a (large/small) _____ amount of CO_2 to dissolve in the liquid.

large

So long as the cap remains on the bottle, the pressure of CO_2 over the solution is _____, and the amount of dissolved CO_2 is large.

high

When the cap is removed from the bottle, the pressure of CO_2 over the solution is _____.

reduced

In agreement with Henry's law, the decreased pressure of CO_2 over the solution _____ the solubility in CO_2 in the solution.

decreases

The bubbles that are seen when a bottle of carbonated beverage is opened are _____.

carbon dioxide gas that is coming out of the solution because of the decreasing solubility of the gas as the pressure is decreased

Many mixtures of economic and industrial importance are composed of liquids. Petroleum is one natural product in this class. Alcohols, ethers, and many other organic compounds are synthesized in solution. These solutions are often separated by *fractional distillation*. Fractional distillation is possible when the liquids have different boiling points; the greater the difference, the more completely and easily is the mixture separated.

Fractional distillation has been developed to a high degree of efficiency in the petroleum industry. The process involves heating the solution and allowing the vapors to pass through a fractionating column. The fractionating column may be simply a glass tube, or it may be packed with a material such as glass helices or wire gauze to provide a surface on which part of the mixed vapor can condense. Figure 9 shows a simple laboratory distillation apparatus. As the liquid runs down into the distillation vessel, a countercurrent flow is established. Vapor goes up and liquid goes down. The liquid with the lowest boiling point reaches the top of the column first. Components, or fractions, may be withdrawn at the top of the column. A condenser is usually attached so that the fraction may be collected as a liquid.

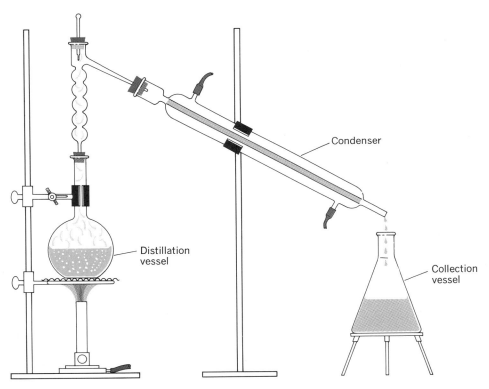

Condenser

Distillation vessel

Collection vessel

Fig. 9 Laboratory apparatus for fractional distillation.

Although very efficient laboratory fractionating columns only a few feet in length have been designed, columns for industrial use, often as much as 100 ft in height, are one of the landmarks of an oil refinery.

Fractional distillation depends on a difference in _____ _____ between the components of a solution.

boiling point or *vapor pressure*

In order for any substance to pass through the fractionating column into the receiver, its vapors must be _____ the boiling point.

at or above

If the vapors of a substance are below the boiling point, they will _____ and drop back to the distillation vessel.

condense to a liquid

Since the source of heat is at the bottom of the column, the temperature _____ toward the top of a fractionating column.

decreases

When solutions of two or more liquids are distilled, each _____ behaves much as if it were present alone in the container.

liquid or *component*

At any temperature, the vapor above the solution contains a relatively larger amount of the component with the _____ equilibrium vapor pressure, or lower boiling point.

higher

As the temperature of the mixture rises during the distillation, the temperature at the top of the column eventually reaches the _____ of one of the components, and this component appears in the distillate.

boiling point

The first component to appear in the distillate will be the one with the _____ boiling point.

lowest

Acetone, an important industrial solvent, boils at 56.2°C. When a solution of acetone in water is distilled, the first fraction of the distillate contains _____ _____.

acetone

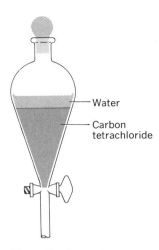

Fig. 10 Two-phase extraction using a separatory funnel.

Another method for separating solutes from solvents is known as *extraction*, or *partition*. The process can best be explained by an example.

Let's consider a solution of bromine in water. These two substances can be separated by distillation, but extraction is somewhat less complicated. Here's how it works: Another solvent that is a good solvent for bromine, but does not dissolve in water, is added. Carbon tetrachloride is such a solvent. The solubility of Br_2 in CCl_4 is 98 g/100 g of solvent, whereas the solubility of Br_2 in water is only 3.5 g/100 g.

Carbon tetrachloride does not dissolve in water to any appreciable extent. The two liquids are immiscible. Consequently, if some carbon tetrachloride is added to a solution of bromine in water and shaken vigorously, the bromine will tend to dissolve in the carbon tetrachloride. When the mixture is allowed to stand for a moment, the carbon tetrachloride settles to the bottom. If the operation has been carried out in a separatory funnel as shown in Fig. 10, the carbon tetrachloride layer can be withdrawn through the stopcock.

Because Br_2 is more soluble in CCl_4 than water, the CCl_4 layer contains a relatively large amount of the _____.

Br_2

If a second quantity of CCl_4 is added, a _____ portion of the Br_2 that is left in the water will dissolve in it.

large

By repeated use of this extraction process, the amount of Br_2 in the aqueous solution can be made extremely _____.

small

Extraction depends on two conditions. One of them is that the _____ to be extracted must be soluble in two different solvents.

solute or component

The second condition is that the two solvents must not _____.

dissolve in each other

Solid benzoic acid is very soluble in ether, but only slightly soluble in water. Water and ether are immiscible. _____ can be used to extract benzoic acid from a(n) _____ solution.

Ether aqueous (water)

Use of the ether in several small portions is better than using one large amount because _____ _____.

each portion extracts a large fraction of the benzoic acid left in the water after the previous portion was used

Many natural products and synthetic compounds are separated and purified by extraction. Similar processes are often used to concentrate the ores of metals.
Yet another widely used method of separation is crystallization. It is one of the best ways to purify solid substances.

The amount of any solid that will dissolve in a solvent is limited; the solid has a definite _____ in the solvent.

solubility

If the solvent is allowed to evaporate from a solution of a solid in a liquid, the solution will eventually become saturated, and the _____ will separate as crystals.

solute (solid)

The "manufacture" of table salt from sea water makes use of _____. The solvent water is evaporated by the energy of the sun.

crystallization

Many solutes are more soluble at high temperatures. If this is the case, crystallization will occur when a saturated solution is _____.

cooled

In order for crystallization to be useful as a means of purifying solid substances, the solubility of the impurities should be _____, and the solubility of the substance should be _____.

high
low

For this reason a chemist may experiment with a number of different _____ when he has the problem of purifying a substance.

solvents

In your laboratory work you have probably already carried out a number of separations of the components of solutions. As you continue to study chemistry, you will come upon many more. The foregoing discussion should help you to understand these separations better as well as to suggest methods you might use to solve experimental problems. In advanced courses you may learn about other methods such as ion exchange, chromatography, and molecular distillation.

2.7 General review

This section is a general review of this chapter on solutions with particular emphasis on problem solving and definition of terms. After each frame you will find the number of the section where you can find additional information if you want it.

Homogeneous chemical systems consist of a single _____ with uniform properties (Sec. 2.1).

phase

A pure substance such as water may form a homogeneous system of one phase or a _____ system of two or more phases (Sec. 2.1).

heterogeneous

Solutions always consist of a single phase and are _____ systems with two or more components (Sec. 2.1).

homogeneous

One component of a solution is usually designated as the solvent; the others are called _____ (Sec. 2.2).

solutes

A solution which is in equilibrium with undissolved solute is said to be _____ (Sec. 2.3).

saturated

A solution of 15 g of Y in 100 g of water is saturated. The _____ of Y in water is 15 g/ 100 g (Sec. 2.3).

solubility

If 10 g of Y is dissolved in 100 g of water, the solution is _____ (Sec. 2.3).

unsaturated

The _____ of a solution expresses the relative amounts of solute and solvent (Sec. 2.4).

concentration

If an aqueous solution contains 60% acetic acid by weight, 250 g of the solution contains _____ g of acetic acid and ____ g of water (Sec. 2.4.1).

150
100

The formula weight of acetic acid is 60.0. There is _____ moles of acetic acid in the 250-g sample considered above.

2.50

There is _____ moles of water in the sample.

$\dfrac{100\ g}{18\ g/mole} = 5.55$

The mole fraction of acetic acid in the solution is _____ (Sec. 2.4.2).

$\dfrac{2.50}{2.50 + 5.55} = 0.31$

The mole fraction of water is _____.

$1.00 - 0.31 = 0.69$

The density of the acetic acid solution is 1.064 g/ml. Its molarity is _____ (Sec. 2.4.3).

10.6

If you missed the last answer, do as many of these frames as you need to get on the right path. If you got it right, go on to the next section.

1 liter of the solution weighs _____ g. $(1.064 \ g/ml)(1,000 \ ml)$
$$= 1,064$$

1 liter of the solution contains _____ g of acetic $(1,064 \ g)(0.60)$
acid. $= 639$

There is _____ moles of acetic acid in 639 g. $\dfrac{639 \ g}{60.0 \ g/mole} = 10.6$

The number of moles of acetic acid per liter of solution,
or the molarity, is _____.   10.6

The molality of a 60% aqueous solution of acetic acid is
_____ (Sec. 2.4.4).   25

If you missed the answer, do as many of these frames as you need to get it.
If you got it right, go on to the next section.

In 100 g of the solution there are _____ g of acetic acid   60
and _____ g of water.   40

60 g of acetic acid is _____ mole(s). $\dfrac{60 \ g}{60 \ g/mole} = 1$

40 g of water is _____ kg. $\dfrac{40 \ g}{1,000 \ g/kg} = 0.04$

Molality is defined as the number of _____ of   *moles*
solute per _____ of solvent.   *kilogram*

The molality of 60% acetic acid is _____. $\dfrac{1.0 \ mole}{0.040 \ kg} = 25$

If 15 ml of this 10.6 *M* solution is diluted to a volume $\dfrac{(15 \ ml)(10.6 \ M)}{(1,000 \ ml)}$
of 1.0 liter, the molarity of the dilute solution is _____
_____ (Sec. 2.4.3). $= 0.16$

Properties of solution that depend on the number of
solute particles are called _____ prop-   *colligative*
erties (Sec. 2.5).

The vapor pressure of a solution is always (lower/higher) _____ than the vapor pressure of the pure solvent (Sec. 2.5).

lower

If vapor-pressure lowering is a colligative property, a concentrated solution will have a (lower/higher) _____ vapor pressure than a dilute solution (Sec. 2.5).

lower

Freezing-point depression is another colligative property. The molal freezing-point depression constant for water is 3.35°F. A solution of 23 g of ethanol (formula wt = 46) in 200 g of water freezes at _____°F (Sec. 2.5.1).

24

If you missed the answer, do these frames. If not, go on to the next section.

The number of moles of ethanol is _____.

$$\frac{23 \ g}{46 \ g/mole} = 0.50$$

The molality of the solution is _____.

$$\frac{0.50 \ mole}{0.20 \ kg} = 2.5$$

The freezing point is lowered by _____°F.

$$(2.5)(3.35) = 8.4$$

Since water normally freezes at 32°F, the freezing point of the solution is _____.

$$32°F - 8°F$$
$$= 24°F$$

The molal boiling-point elevation constant for water is 0.94°F. The 2.50 *m* solution above should boil at ____°F (Sec. 2.5.2).

$$212 + (2.5)(0.94)$$
$$= 214.3$$

Another colligative property of solutions is responsible for the rise of sap in trees and many other biological processes. It is _____ (Sec. 2.5.3).

osmotic pressure

References

Andrews, D. H., and R. J. Kokes, "Fundamental Chemistry," 2d ed., chap. 10, pp. 246–279, Wiley, New York, 1965.

Gregg, D. C., "Principles of Chemistry," 2d ed., chap. 16, pp. 366–397, Allyn and Bacon, Boston, 1963.

Mahan, B. H., "University Chemistry," chap. 4, pp. 126–144, Addison-Wesley, Reading, Mass., 1965.

Pauling, L., "College Chemistry," 3d ed., chap. 17, pp. 468–481, Freeman, San Francisco, 1964.

Quagliano, J. V., "Chemistry," 2d ed., chaps. 15 and 16, pp. 351–387, Prentice-Hall, Englewood Cliffs, N.J., 1963.

Sienko, M. J., and R. A. Plane, "Chemistry," 3d ed., chap. 10, pp. 207–245, McGraw-Hill, New York, 1966.

Sienko, M. J., and R. A. Plane, "Chemistry: Principles and Properties," chap. 8, pp. 173–199, McGraw-Hill, New York, 1966.

Sisler, H. H., C. A. VanderWerf, and A. W. Davidson, "College Chemistry: A Systematic Approach," 2d ed., chap. 13, pp. 215 236, Macmillan, New York, 1961.

Timm, J. A., "General Chemistry," 4th ed., chap. 19, pp. 241–268, McGraw-Hill, New York, 1966.

chapter three # solutions of electrolytes

Scientific theories rank among the major achievements of the human mind. You have already learned about the atomic theory, the kinetic-molecular theory, and the theory of atomic periodicity. To these we can now add the theory of electrolytic dissociation, first stated in 1887 by the Swedish chemist, Svante Arrhenius.

Scientific theories often follow a similar pattern of development. Experimental observations accumulate until a genius like Dalton or Mendeleev sees the link that joins them all together and formulates a theory, which is then tested by many other scientists. If it withstands the tests and is useful for the prediction of new facts, the scientific community accepts the theory, and its discoverer takes a place among the great men of science.

Sometimes refined measurements or the discovery of new phenomena yields facts that are in disagreement with the theory. The original theory can usually be modified to accommodate them, but it may have to be discarded forever as was the phlogiston theory. All the theories mentioned in the first paragraph stand in the position of having been restated and firmly established.

To give you some taste of the discovery of a scientific theory, we will first examine some of the observations that led Arrhenius to his theory.

3.1 Electrolytes

You remember that the freezing-point depression of a solution can be used to measure the molecular weight of the solute. The depression of the freezing point is a colligative property, which depends only on the number of particles of solute and not on their chemical nature. Although this method gives satisfactory results for solutions of many solutes, there are several types of solutes for which it gives incorrect molecular weights.

An example is common table salt, or sodium chloride, with the formula NaCl. On the basis of your present knowledge, you would expect that 1 mole of NaCl (58.5 g) dissolved in 1 kg of water would make a solution that would freeze at $-1.86°C$. The actual freezing point is $-3.5°C$, a depression of nearly twice the expected amount. Such anomalous depressions of the freezing point are observed for many solutes dissolved in water. The same is true for a few other solvents. On the other hand, the same solutes give normal freezing-point depressions when dissolved in benzene and some other similar solvents.

Now put yourself in Arrhenius's place. Which of these is the most valid conclusion to be drawn from the observation that a 1 m solution of sodium chloride freezes at $-3.5°C$?

The formula NaCl does not properly represent sodium chloride. Its formula weight must be less than 58.5.	Go to A below
When it dissolves in water, 1 mole of NaCl must break up into more than 1 mole of solute particles.	Go to B below
When it dissolves in benzene, NaCl gives a normal freezing-point depression.	Go to C below

A

Incorrect. Are you going to throw out all you know about chemical formulas because of one new observation? All the studies of NaCl crystals certainly indicate that the formula NaCl is adequate. The whole structure of the atomic-weight scale has been confirmed by countless observations. The formula weight of NaCl is certainly 58.5.

The fact that a 1 m aqueous solution of NaCl freezes at $-3.5°C$ does throw a monkey wrench into our ideas about freezing-point depression, but there ought to be another conclusion that doesn't force us to cast aside so much hard-won knowledge. Go back and choose another answer.

B

Right. When it dissolves in water, 1 mole of NaCl must break up into more than 1 mole of solute particles. Since the freezing-point depression depends on the number of particles, these additional particles account for the increased depression. Go to the paragraph following C (page 106).

c

You are wrong. You must learn to distinguish between an observation and a conclusion as well as to apply only pertinent observations when you try to draw a conclusion. The fact that NaCl gives a normal freezing-point depression when it is dissolved in benzene is an experimental observation. The situation that you are considering, however, involves an aqueous solution. Observations on benzene solutions are not pertinent. Go back and read the problem again.

Freezing-point depressions that are larger than normal are one of the key points in the Arrhenius theory. Boiling-point elevations, osmotic pressures, and other colligative properties are similarly affected.

Another experimental observation that Arrhenius sought to explain was that all the solutions that give unusually large freezing-point depressions also conduct an electric current. Figure 11 shows a simple device for testing the electrical conductivity of solutions. The electrodes are strips of metal, usually nickel or platinum.

The device is constructed so that both the light bulb and the solution in the beaker are part of the electric circuit. In order for the lamp to light, there must be a complete electrical circuit. This means that all parts of the circuit, including the solution, must be conductors.

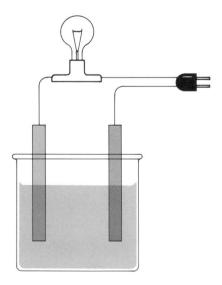

Fig. 11 Simple apparatus for measuring conductivity of solutions.

If the lamp lights when the electrodes are dipped in a solution, the solution (is/is not) _____ a conductor.

is

If the solution does not conduct current, the lamp (will/will not) _____ light.

will not

Solutions of NaCl and other solutes which give abnormally large freezing-point depressions (do/do not) _____ conduct current.

do

When sugar solutions, which give normal freezing-point depressions, are tested for conductivity, the lamp (does/does not) _____ light.

does not

Suppose you have a 0.25 m solution which freezes at $-0.90°C$. Would you expect it to conduct a current? _____

Yes

Solutes that yield electrically conducting solutions are called *electrolytes*. Solutes that yield nonconducting solutions are called *nonelectrolytes*. Electrolytes may be further classified as strong or weak according to whether they are good or poor conductors.

Solutions do not conduct current in the same way that metals such as silver or copper do. When metals conduct current, there is no observable chemical change. This is called *metallic conductivity*. The conductivity of electrolytes is always accompanied by chemical changes. You may have seen the decomposition of water by electrolysis. The decomposition is a chemical change that accompanies the electric current. If you observe the surface of the electrodes in the apparatus used to test conductivity, you can usually see the formation of bubbles, which is evidence of chemical reaction. This kind of conductivity is called *electrolytic conductivity*.

Still another way in which solutions of electrolytes differ from those of nonelectrolytes is in the velocity of their reactions. In general, reactions between solutions of electrolytes are much faster than reactions between solutions of nonelectrolytes. When solutions of the electrolytes sodium chloride and silver nitrate are mixed, a precipitate of silver chloride is formed at once. Many reactions in organic chemistry that involve solutions of nonelectrolytes require long periods of heating in order to give significant amounts of the desired product. This slow rate of reaction is sometimes an advantage. The destructive oxidation of automobile antifreeze solutions is very slow because the solutions are nonelectrolytes. You will encounter many examples of the rapid reactions of solutions of electrolytes in your laboratory work in general chemistry. In fact, many of your experiments are designed to take advantage of this fact.

3.2 The Arrhenius theory of electrolytic dissociation

Any theoretical explanation of the difference between electrolytes and nonelectrolytes must explain the three major differences between their solutions: (1) anomalous freezing-point depression of electrolytes; (2) electrolytic conductivity; and (3) the rapid reactions of electrolytes. It should also account for the existence of strong and weak electrolytes.

Arrhenius proposed such a theory in 1887. The magnitude of his achievement is brought into perspective when we note that the electron had not been identified at that time and nothing was known about atomic structure or the nature of ionic crystals.

Arrhenius worked out his theory as part of his thesis for the doctor's degree. Because of its novelty, he expected that it would be met by opposition, and for this reason he expressed his conclusions in a circumspect fashion. The realization of his expectations is illustrated by this passage from his journal.[1]

I had, in this manner, deduced a rather large number of different properties which had not been explained before; but I must say that this circumstance made no very great impression upon my professors in Upsala.

I came to my professor, Cleve, whom I admire very much, and I said: "I have a new theory of electrical conductivity as a cause of chemical reactions." He said: "That is very interesting," and then said "Good-by." He explained to me later, when he had to pronounce the reason for my receiving the Nobel prize for that work, that he knew very well that there are so many different theories formed, and that they are all almost certain to be wrong, for after a short time they disappear, and, therefore, by using a statistical manner of forming his ideas, he concluded that my theory also would not last very long.

Opposition to the theory was strong, and nearly twenty years were required for all the skeptics to be won over. Although we will see that it had to be modified in the light of some twentieth-century discoveries, we can use it to account for some of the familiar properties of electrolytes.

Arrhenius theorized that solutions of electrolytes contain electrically charged particles called ions (*eye*-uns). We now know that ions are atoms or groups of atoms that have gained or lost electrons.

The chemical change represented by this equation,

$$Na \rightarrow Na^+ + e$$

is the formation of a sodium _____ from a sodium atom.   *ion*

[1] Svante Arrhenius, Electrolytic Dissociation, *J. Am. Chem. Soc.,* **34**:360, 1912. Reprinted by permission of the American Chemical Society.

In the change shown above, the sodium atom loses a(n) _____ to form a positively charged sodium ion.

electron

This equation represents the _____ of an electron by a chlorine atom to form a negatively charged chloride ion:

gain

$$Cl + e \rightarrow Cl^-$$

There are two kinds of ions: cations (*cat-eye-uns*) and anions (*anne-eye-uns*). Cations bear a positive charge. Na^+ is a(n) _____.

cation

From this it follows that anions must bear _____ _____ charges. Cl^- is an anion.

negative

K^+, Mg^{++}, and NH_4^+ are all _____ that are formed when electrons are _____.

cations
lost

When atoms or groups of atoms _____ electrons, _____ such as Br^-, $SO_4^=$, and NO_3^- are formed.

gain
anions

As a typical example of an electrolyte, let's once again consider a solution of NaCl in water. Arrhenius assumed that under the influence of water, ions of sodium and chlorine become free to move independently and so give rise to the electrical conductivity of the solution. Under the influence of an electric current, the positive sodium ions soon collect around the negative electrode, called the cathode. Negative ions collect around the positive electrode, or anode. Incidentally, this is the basis for the names of the ions: *cat*ions collect at the cathode; *an*ions at the anode. Figure 12 illustrates this action for a solution of NaCl in water.

Since the motion of electrically charged particles constitutes an electric current, the Arrhenius theory gives at least a qualitative explanation of electrolytic conductivity. You will recall that the difference between metallic and electrolytic conductivity is that a chemical change accompanies the latter. When an aqueous solution of NaCl conducts a current, chlorine gas is formed at the anode, and hydrogen gas is formed at the cathode.

The migration of cations and anions can be demonstrated dramatically with a solution of copper(II) permanganate, $Cu(MnO_4)_2$. The solution has a magenta

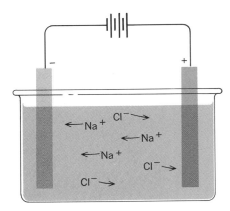

Fig. 12 Movement of ions during electrolysis of aqueous solution of NaCl.

color. The experiment may be set up in a U tube as shown in Fig. 13. The magenta solution of copper(II) permanganate is placed at the bottom of the U tube. The surface is covered with a colorless electrolyte such as nitric acid, and care is taken not to let it mix with the copper permanganate solution. When a source of current is connected to the two electrodes, visible changes are soon observed.

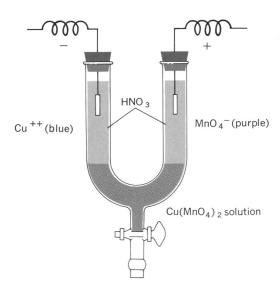

Fig. 13 Electrolysis of an aqueous solution of $Cu(MnO_4)_2$.

The colorless solution in the cathode (left) arm of the U tube becomes blue, and the solution in the anode arm becomes magenta. This movement of color indicates the presence of _____.

ions

Current in solutions of electrolytes is carried by ions. _____ move toward the cathode, and _____ _____ move toward the anode.

Cations; anions

The cation in a solution of copper(II) permanganate is recognized by the color _____.

blue

On the other hand, since the magenta color moves toward the anode, it must be characteristic of the _____ _____ in the solution.

anion

If copper(II) permanganate dissociates in water to give Cu^{++} and MnO_4^- ions, the blue color is caused by the presence of _____, the cation.

Cu^{++}

The anion _____ causes the magenta color.

MnO_4^-

Solutions of copper(II) permanganate appear magenta because the color of the MnO_4^- ion obscures the _____ _____.

blue color of the Cu^{++} *ion*

If solutions of copper(II) chloride or copper(II) nitrate were electrolyzed in a similar way, one would expect to see _____ color move to the cathode.

a blue

Close observation of the electrodes should reveal evidence of a(n) _____.

chemical change

Another difference between solutions of electrolytes and nonelectrolytes that the theory must explain is the rapid rate of the reactions of electrolytes. As you know, a chemical reaction involves the rearrangement of chemical bonds. Some are broken and others are formed. In the last chapter you learned that atoms and molecules must be activated in order to react. This takes time. Consequently, even in solution, reactions of molecules proceed at a comparatively slow rate. By contrast, solutions of electrolytes generally react almost instantaneously. For instance, when solutions of sodium chloride and silver nitrate are mixed, a white precipitate of silver chloride appears at once. The reaction might be written

$$NaCl + AgNO_3 \rightarrow AgCl\downarrow + NaNO_3$$

When presented in this way, it is hard to see why the reaction should be any more rapid than when the same substances are mixed together dry. It would appear that the NaCl and $AgNO_3$ would have to decompose and then reassemble as AgCl and $NaNO_3$. If, however, the NaCl and $AgNO_3$ are present in the solutions as ions, the reason for the rapid reaction becomes easy to see. It can be written

$$Na^+ + Cl^- + Ag^+ + NO_3^- \rightarrow AgCl + Na^+ + NO_3^-$$

All that happens is the union of the Ag^+ and Cl^- ions. Ions that are already present react when the two solutions are mixed. No energy of activation is needed. Since they do not actually participate in the reaction, the Na^+ and NO_3^- are called *spectator ions*. The actual chemical change can be written

$$Ag^+ + Cl^- \rightarrow AgCl\downarrow$$

You should not accept the statement that the Na^+ and NO_3^- do not participate in the reaction without some evidence. Which of the following is the *best* evidence that the statement is true?

When the solution is evaporated after the removal of AgCl, solid $NaNO_3$ is recovered.	Go to A below
The precipitate is found to contain some $NaNO_3$ as well as AgCl.	Go to B below
Even after the AgCl precipitate is removed, the solution still conducts electric current.	Go to C below

A

You are incorrect. Recovery of solid $NaNO_3$ is certainly an indication that Na^+ and NO_3^- do not participate in the precipitation of AgCl. But does it prove that they do not combine to form $NaNO_3$ molecules that remain in solution?

$$Na^+ + NO_3^- \rightarrow NaNO_3(soln)$$

It doesn't, does it? To prove that the Na^+ and NO_3^- ions take no part in the reaction, you need evidence of their presence in the solution after the AgCl precipitates. Go back and find it.

B

You are wrong. Wouldn't the appearance of $NaNO_3$ in the precipitate along with AgCl indicate that Na^+ and NO_3^- had indeed reacted with one another?

$$Na^+ + NO_3^- \rightarrow NaNO_3\downarrow$$

To prove that the Na^+ and NO_3^- ions take no part in the reaction, you need evidence of their presence in the solution after the AgCl precipitates. Go back and find it.

C

Right. The fact that the solution still conducts electric current after the AgCl is removed is strong proof that some ions are still present in the solution. Go on to the next paragraph.

The third property of solutions of electrolytes explained by the Arrhenius theory of electrolytic dissociation is the unusually large freezing-point depression. You will recall that the freezing-point depression of a 1 m solution of NaCl is 3.5°C, nearly twice the expected 1.86°C.

Like all the colligative properties, freezing-point depression depends on the _____ of solute particles, not their identity or nature.	*number*
If NaCl dissociates into Na^+ and Cl^- ions when it dissolves, 1 mole of NaCl should provide _____ of solute particles.	2 *moles*
If it is completely dissociated, the freezing-point depression of a 1 m solution of NaCl should be _____°C.	3.72
Apparently, 1 mole of NaCl is not quite so effective as _____ moles of nonelectrolyte.	2

In fact, the freezing-point depression per mole of NaCl increases as solutions are made more dilute. This table shows the trend.

Concentration of NaCl	Observed freezing point, °C	Freezing-point depression per mole NaCl, °C
0.1 m	−0.347	3.47
0.01 m	−0.0361	3.61
0.001 m	−0.00366	3.66
0.0001 m	−0.000372	3.72

Arrhenius explained this increase by postulating that the degree of dissociation increased as the solutions were made more dilute. That is, NaCl is completely dissociated into Na^+ and Cl^- in a 0.0001 m solution but less than completely dissociated in a more concentrated solution.

This same explanation could be offered for the existence of weak electrolytes. If they are only slightly dissociated, they will cause only a slightly greater freezing-point depression than the same concentration of a nonelectrolyte.

The extent of dissociation of solutes varies widely. Some, such as NaCl, HCl, and HNO_3, are essentially completely dissociated into ions in aqueous solution and are strong electrolytes. Others, such as acetic acid, are only slightly dissociated and are called weak electrolytes.

The percent of dissociation can be determined by measuring any property of the solution that depends on the concentration of ions. As an example, let's consider a solution of the weak electrolyte AB in water.

The observed freezing point of a 0.0100 m solution of AB is −0.0193°C. What percent of the AB molecules have been dissociated by the water? *Note:* Use three significant figures in your calculations for this series of frames.

If some of the AB molecules dissociate into A^+ and B^- ions, the solution contains three kinds of particles: undissociated _____ molecules, _____ ions, and _____ ions.

AB; A^+; B^-

Every AB molecule, A^+ ion, and B^- ion contributes equally to the _____ _____.

freezing-point depression

Since 1 mole of solute particles will lower the freezing point 1.86°C, exactly _____ mole(s) of solute particles will lower it 0.0193°C.

$\dfrac{0.0193}{1.86} = 0.0104$

Thus, in a 0.0100 m solution of AB, there must be 0.0104 mole of _____ per kg of water.

The total number of particles is made up of _____ _____.

Before any dissociation takes place, a 0.0100 m solution of AB contains _____ of AB molecules per kg of water.

If we let d represent the number of moles of AB that dissociate, the number of moles of AB remaining after dissociation is _____ mole(s)/kg of water.

For each molecule of AB that dissociates, _____ A$^+$ ion and _____ B$^-$ ion are produced.

If d moles of AB dissociate, _____ moles of A$^+$ and _____ moles of B$^-$ are produced.

The total number of solute particles per kg of water, as indicated by the freezing point, is exactly _____. That is, [AB] + [A$^+$] + [B$^-$] = _____.

In terms of d, this total is composed of _____ moles of AB, _____ moles of A$^+$, and _____ moles of B$^-$.

Algebraically, $(0.0100 - d) + d + d = 0.0104$, or $d =$ _____.

This means that a 0.0100 m AB solution contains 0.004 mole of A$^+$, _____ mole of B$^-$, and _____ mole of undissociated AB per kg of water.

The fraction of AB molecules dissociated is equal to the number that do dissociate divided by the total number available, or _____.

Multiplying the fraction by 100, we learn that a 0.0100 m solution of AB is ____% dissociated.

Numerous measurements on various electrolytes under many conditions indicate that the percent dissociation depends on four factors: (1) the nature of the solute; (2) the nature of the solvent; (3) the temperature; and (4) the concentration of the solute.

We have already noted that the nature of some solutes causes them to be strong electrolytes, whereas others are weak electrolytes. The effect of the solvent is also important. Earlier we saw that NaCl is a strong electrolyte in water but a nonelectrolyte in benzene.

As the temperature is raised, the percent dissociation of some substances increases. For others it decreases, and for still others there is no change. There is no simple way to predict the change for any given electrolyte.

The percent dissociation of all electrolytes increases as the concentration decreases. This table summarizes measurements of the percent dissociation of acetic acid into hydrogen and acetate ions in aqueous solutions of various concentrations. (The data are also shown in Fig. 14.)

Concentration of acetic acid	Percent dissociation
1 M	0.4
0.1 M	1.3
0.01 M	4.3
0.001 M	15
0.00001 M	75

Can you imagine an almost infinitely dilute solution of one molecule of acetic acid in a swimming pool full of water? When it dissociates, the probability that the ions will come together again is practically nil. Since the single molecule is dissociated, the percent dissociation is 100. As they approach infinite dilution, all electrolytes approach 100% dissociation.

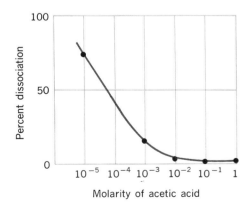

Fig. 14 Percent dissociation of acetic acid.

If you have followed this discussion closely, you are probably wondering how we can distinguish between strong and weak electrolytes if all electrolytes are nearly completely dissociated in very low concentrations. The apparent difficulty is overcome by adopting the convention that a 1 M solution be used for comparison. If the substance is highly dissociated in a 1 M solution, it is termed a strong electrolyte. If it is only slightly dissociated at this concentration, it is called a weak electrolyte.

At least a rough idea of the degree of conductivity of a solution can be gotten from the device shown in Fig. 11. The bulb lights dimly for weak electrolytes and brightly for strong electrolytes.

When tested for conductivity, a solution of alcohol and water does not cause the bulb to light. The solution (does/does not) _____ conduct electrical current.

does not

A 1 M solution of HCl causes the bulb to burn brightly. HCl is a (strong/weak) _____ electrolyte.

strong

Acetic acid is a weak electrolyte. The conductivity of a 1 M solution of acetic acid is _____.

small (or *low*)

A very dilute solution of HCl, say 0.001 M, is a (good/poor) _____ conductor.

poor

Still, a 0.001 M solution of HCl is a better conductor than a 0.001 M solution of a _____ electrolyte such as acetic acid.

weak

Measurement of conductivity alone does not let us decide whether a solute is a strong or weak electrolyte. We must know the _____ of the solution being tested.

concentration

Up to this point, the original Arrhenius theory explains the behavior of all solutions of both strong and weak electrolytes. A twentieth-century discovery, however, required a modification. You will remember that fairly concentrated solutions of NaCl do not appear to be 100 % dissociated into Na^+ and Cl^- ions if freezing-point depression is used as the criterion. Modern research has proved beyond reasonable doubt that solid crystals of NaCl are composed of Na^+ and Cl^- ions. There are no NaCl molecules. When it dissolves, NaCl must be 100 % dissociated.

An explanation of this apparent contradiction was offered in 1923 by the Dutch chemist Debye and his German colleague, Hückel.

In aqueous solutions of strong electrolytes, the ions are separated, on the average, by many water molecules. In this respect they are completely dissociated and should lower the freezing point of water by some multiple of the normal amount. As we know, however, they do not.

The Debye-Hückel theory of interionic attraction of electrolytes accounts for this effect. Since the solute particles of electrolytes carry electrical charges, there are attractions between ions of opposite charge even though they are separated by water molecules. The positive and negative ions in a solution of a strong electrolyte such as NaCl do not act totally independently of one another. For this reason, 1 mole of NaCl is less effective than 2 moles of a nonelectrolyte.

The attraction between ions of opposite charge decreases rapidly as the distance separating them increases. In dilute solutions, the ions are far apart, and the attractions are small. The table on page 114 shows that dilute solutions conform better to our expectations.

Sodium chloride is a strong electrolyte in water, but a weak electrolyte in ether. These facts are evidence that dissociation of electrolytes depends on the _____ _____.	*solvent*
Since the degree of dissociation of a solute is really an expression of the point of equilibrium, it (might/might not) _____ be expected to depend on the temperature of the solution.	*might*
The difference in conductivity between 0.001 M solutions of hydrochloric acid and acetic acid is (more/less) _____ than the difference between 1 M solutions of the two solutes.	*less*

Before we go on to learn about different kinds of electrolytes, let's review some of the new words in your vocabulary.

If a solution conducts electric current, the solute is called a(n) _____.	*electrolyte*
Reactions between solutions of electrolytes are usually faster than reactions between solutions of _____.	*nonelectrolytes*

Electrolytic conductivity is always accompanied by chemical _____.

reaction or *change*

Solutions of electrolytes contain charged particles called _____.

ions

A solution of KNO_3 in water is a good conductor of electric current. When it dissolves, KNO_3 dissociates into _____ cations and _____ anions.

K^+; NO_3^- (in this order)

Some solutes, such as acetic acid, do not dissociate completely in solution. They are called _____ electrolytes.

weak

The relative, or percent, dissociation of weak electrolytes increases as the concentration _____.

decreases

3.3 Acids and bases

Nearly all electrolytes belong to one of three groups of substances: acids, bases, or salts. This section is devoted to a study of acids and bases. Salts will be discussed in a later section.

You should already be familiar with a number of substances whose aqueous solutions are called acids. Among them are HCl, HNO_3, and H_2SO_4. Acetic acid, whose formula is $HC_2H_3O_2$, was cited in the last section as an example of a weak acid. Other substances, such as NaOH, KOH, and NH_3, are familiar to you as bases.

One way to recognize acids and bases is by their properties. Acids generally have a sour taste. Bases, on the other hand, may have a bitter taste. Acids cause the purple dye litmus to turn pink. Bases cause the litmus to turn blue, and their solutions have a greasy, or slippery, feel.

The sour taste of citrus fruits indicates that they contain _____.

acids

If a piece of blue litmus paper is moistened with vinegar, it turns _____ because vinegar is acidic.

pink

If litmus paper turns blue when moistened with a solution, the solution is said to be _____.

basic

To learn more about the chemical properties of acids and bases, we must begin with the properties of water. In the last section water was assumed to be a nonelectrolyte. Very careful measurements, however, show that it conducts electric current to a very slight extent.

For this reason, water should be classed as a(n) _____ _____ electrolyte.

(very) weak

Electrolytic conductivity results from the presence of _____ in solutions of electrolytes.

ions

Solutions of electrolytes are electrically neutral. They must contain equal numbers of positive _____ and negative _____.

cations
anions

There is no solute in pure water. If it is a very weak electrolyte, the ions that are present must be provided by the _____ itself.

water

The electrolytic dissociation of water must produce both positive and negative ions in order to maintain _____ neutrality.

electrical

This equation represents the dissociation of water:

$$H_2O \rightarrow H^+ + OH^-$$

It splits into a positive *hydrogen* ion and a(n) _____ _____ *hydroxide* ion.

negative

The equation is sometimes written this way:

$$H_2O + H_2O \rightarrow H_3O^+ + OH^-$$

In this case one assumes that when two water molecules collide, a proton (H^+) is transferred from one oxygen atom to the other. An electron-dot representation would be this:

$$H : \overset{..}{\underset{..}{O}} : \; + \; H : \overset{..}{\underset{..}{O}} : \; \rightarrow \; \left[H : \overset{..}{\underset{..}{O}} : H \right]^+ \; + \; \left[: \overset{..}{\underset{..}{O}} : H \right]^-$$
$$\;\;\;\; H \qquad\qquad H \qquad\qquad\quad H$$

Since both the ions are surrounded by water molecules, the dissociation is usually written as

$$H_2O \rightarrow H^+ + OH^-$$

The symbols H^+ and H_3O^+ are used interchangeably by most chemists and many textbook writers. In this program we will use H^+, but you should bear in mind that both H^+ and H_3O^+ represent hydrogen ions in solution surrounded by water molecules.

The degree of dissociation of water is extremely small. In pure water the concentration of hydrogen ion is 1.0×10^{-7} M. The concentration of hydroxide ion is also _____. Each water molecule which dissociates forms one _____ and one _____.

1.0×10^{-7}
H^+; OH^-

The density of water at room temperature is about 1 g/ml. 1 liter of water, then, is about _____ g.

1,000

There is _____ moles of water in 1 liter.

$$\frac{1,000 \ g/liter}{18 \ g/mole} = 55$$

The fraction of water molecules dissociated at room temperature is _____.

$$\frac{1.0 \times 10^{-7}}{55}$$
$$= 2 \times 10^{-9}$$

The percent of water molecules dissociated at room temperature is _____.

$(2 \times 10^{-9})(100)$
$= 2 \times 10^{-7}$

Only 1 out of every 500 million water molecules is dissociated. Although this number may seem small enough to be trivial, it is one of water's most important chemical properties. Many of the body's vital reactions depend on the H^+ or OH^- concentrations in the system.

Acids and bases are substances that upset the hydrogen-ion–hydroxide-ion balance of pure water.

An acid increases the hydrogen-ion concentration; a base increases the _____-ion concentration.

hydroxide

The hydrogen ion may be written H_3O^+ or just _____. H_3O^+ is also called the hydronium ion.

H^+

Strong acids such as HCl are completely or almost completely _____ into H+ and negative ions.   *dissociated*

Acetic acid, $HC_2H_3O_2$, is a weak acid. It is only slightly dissociated into hydrogen ions and acetate ions when dissolved in _____.   *water*

NaOH is a strong base and is highly dissociated into Na+ and _____ when dissolved in OH^- (*hydroxide*)
water.

Whether a compound is an acid or base is not always apparent from its formula. It is particularly hazardous to assume that any molecule with an OH group is a base. The substance $SO_2(OH)_2$, for instance, contains two OH groups. Yet when it is dissolved in water, the solution exhibits typical acid properties. The molecule dissociates into H+ and $SO_2(OH)O^-$ ions. To emphasize its acid properties, the formula for the molecule is usually written H_2SO_4 and the negative ion as HSO_4^-. The dissociation equation is

$$H_2SO_4 \rightarrow H^+ + HSO_4^-$$

You probably recognize it now as sulfuric acid.

The formulas of acids are usually written with the available hydrogen ions first. Thus, the formula for acetic acid is written as $HC_2H_3O_2$ to indicate that one of the four hydrogen atoms will dissociate in water as a hydrogen ion.

Household bleach contains hypochlorous acid. Should its formula be written ClOH or HOCl? _____   HOCl

The molecular formula for phosphoric acid is $PO(OH)_3$. Since it contains three available protons, it is better written _____. H_3PO_4

Not all formulas that end with OH are _____.   *bases*
$Ca(OH)_2$ is a base, but CH_3OH is not.

The ultimate decision on the nature of a substance depends on _____   *the properties of its*
_____.   *aqueous solution*

If acids are defined as substances that increase the H^+ concentration in water and bases as substances that increase the OH^- concentration, there are two important implications that should be emphasized. The first is that the definition applies only to aqueous solutions. The second is that substances that do not contain hydrogen may be acids. Likewise, bases may not furnish OH^- directly.

For example, when SO_2 is dissolved in water, this reaction takes place: $SO_2 + H_2O \rightarrow H^+ + HSO_3^-$. According to our definition, SO_2 is an acid.

When ammonia, NH_3, dissolves in water, this reaction takes place:

$$NH_3 + H_2O \rightarrow NH_4^+ + OH^-$$

Ammonia is a(n) —————————.   *base*

The reaction is sometimes written this way:

$$NH_3 + H_2O \rightarrow NH_4OH \rightarrow NH_4^+ + OH^-$$

There is considerable evidence to indicate that the species NH_4OH does not really exist in the solution. The ultimate result of NH_4^+ and OH^- ions is the same, as you can see. Just remember that both equations represent the dissociation of ammonia when it dissolves in water:

$$NH_3 + H_2O \rightarrow NH_4^+ + OH^-$$
$$NH_4OH \rightarrow NH_4^+ + OH^-$$

Carbon dioxide, CO_2, behaves as an acid when dissolved in water. This equation best represents the situation: $CO_2 + H_2O \rightarrow$ ——— $+ HCO_3^-$. H^+

In general, oxides of nonmetallic elements (for example, SO_2 and CO_2) exhibit ————————— properties when dissolved in water.   *acid*

This reaction occurs when Na_2O, sodium oxide, dissolves in water: $Na_2O + H_2O \rightarrow 2Na^+ + 2\,OH^-$. Na_2O behaves as a —————————.   *base*

Without citing more specific examples, we can make the general statement that oxides or nonmetals are _____ and oxides of _____ are bases.

acids; metals

Some other substances affect the H^+ and OH^- concentrations in water in a less obvious fashion. When sulfides such as Na_2S dissolve in water, there is an increase in hydroxide-ion concentration caused by the reaction

$$S^= + H_2O \rightarrow OH^- + SH^-$$

Likewise, ammonium compounds and some aluminum compounds cause an increase in hydrogen-ion concentration. These equations illustrate the effect:

$$NH_4^+ + H_2O \rightarrow NH_3 + H_3O^+$$
$$Al^{3+} + H_2O \rightarrow H^+ + AlOH^{++}$$

These reactions are sometimes called hydrolysis reactions.

There are other definitions for acids and bases that apply to aqueous solutions and to systems that contain no water at all. One of these is the *Brønsted-Lowry definition*.

According to this concept, an acid is any substance that can donate a proton; a base, as you might expect, is any substance that can accept a proton. For example, when ammonium chloride and sodium amide are dissolved in liquid ammonia (NH_3), this reaction occurs:

$$NH_4^+ + NH_2^- \rightarrow 2NH_3$$

The Cl^- and Na^+ are spectator ions.

In this reaction the NH_4^+ donates a proton to the NH_2^-. The Brønsted-Lowry acid is NH_4^+; NH_2^- is a Brønsted-Lowry base.

Returning to aqueous solutions, let's consider HCl, which we have classed as a(n) _____.

strong acid

It reacts with water as shown by the equation $HCl + H_2O \rightarrow H_3O^+ + Cl^-$. HCl is a Brønsted-Lowry _____ also because it donates a proton to H_2O.

acid

When water accepts the proton from HCl in the reaction above, it acts as a Brønsted-Lowry _____.

base

In the Brønsted-Lowry view, water may be both an acid and a base. You will remember that the slight dissociation of water may be represented by the equation $H_2O + H_2O \rightarrow$ _____ + _____.

H_3O^+; OH^-

Water acts as a proton donor to leave _____.

OH^-

Water acts as a proton acceptor to form _____.

H_3O^+

The H_3O^+ ion can be a proton donor, and the OH^- can be a proton acceptor. Suppose we write the last equation in the reverse direction.

$$H_3O^+ + OH^- \rightarrow H_2O + H_2O$$

The hydronium ion donates a proton to the hydroxide ion.

Acid-base pairs that differ only by the presence or absence of the proton are known as *conjugate pairs*. When a Brønsted-Lowry acid donates a proton, it becomes the conjugate base. Referring to the reaction above, we can say that H_2O is the conjugate base of the acid H_3O^+. Likewise, H_3O^+ is the conjugate acid of the base H_2O. Similarly, H_2O is the conjugate acid of the base OH^-, or OH^- is the conjugate base of the acid H_2O. To emphasize this conjugate-pair relationship, equations are often written this way.

$$\underset{\text{acid}_1}{H_3O^+} + \underset{\text{base}_2}{OH^-} \rightarrow \underset{\text{base}_1}{H_2O} + \underset{\text{acid}_2}{H_2O}$$

The subscripts indicate the two conjugate acid-base pairs. Pair 1 is H_3O^+-H_2O; pair 2 is H_2O-OH^-.

Let's see if the Brønsted-Lowry definitions agree with our previous definitions.

We've called HCl an acid. In this reaction

$$HCl + H_2O \rightarrow H_3O^+ + Cl^-$$

HCl donates a proton to _____.

H_2O

The conjugate base of HCl is _____.

Cl^-

The other conjugate pair is H_2O-H_3O^+. The base is _____.

H_2O

Solutions containing the $S^=$ ion exhibit basic properties. If the reaction with water is represented by the equation $S^= + H_2O \rightarrow OH^- + SH^-$, the sulfide ion is a(n) _____.

base

The conjugate acid of the base $S^=$ is _____.

SH^-

Finally, let's review the reaction between NH_4^+ and NH_2^- in the nonaqueous solvent liquid ammonia. The equation for the reaction is $NH_4^+ + NH_2^- \rightarrow 2NH_3$. NH_4^+ is a(n) _____; its conjugate is _____.

acid; NH_3

NH_2^- is a(n) _____; its conjugate is _____.

base; NH_3

There is one more definition of acids and bases that you may encounter. It is the *Lewis definition*. It is based on the current belief that chemical bonds are formed by the sharing of pairs of electrons or the transfer of electrons. A Lewis acid is any chemical species that functions as an electron-pair acceptor in a chemical reaction; an electron-pair donor is a Lewis base. This definition is compatible with both of our other definitions. For example, in the reaction

$$H^+ + \left[\begin{array}{c} \cdot\cdot \\ : Cl : \\ \cdot\cdot \end{array} \right]^- \rightarrow H : \underset{\cdot\cdot}{\overset{\cdot\cdot}{Cl}} :$$

the Lewis acid H^+ accepts an electron pair from the Lewis base Cl^-.

All three definitions are useful to chemists. The first one, however, has the greatest value to the beginning student, who is primarily concerned with aqueous solutions. Therefore, we'll consider an acid to be any substance that increases the H^+ concentration and a base to be any substance that causes an increase in the concentration of OH^-.

When HNO_3 dissolves in water, it dissociates completely into H^+ and NO_3^- ions. It is a(n) _____.

strong acid

In this reaction Li_2O acts as a(n) _____.

base

$$Li_2O + H_2O \rightarrow 2Li^+ + 2\,OH^-$$

The base in this reaction is _____ and the acid
is _____.

$$H-\overset{\overset{\displaystyle O}{\|}}{C}-OH + H_2O \rightarrow H_3O^+ + H-\overset{\overset{\displaystyle O}{\|}}{C}-O^-$$

$H-\overset{\overset{\displaystyle O}{\|}}{C}-O^-$ or H_2O

$H-\overset{\overset{\displaystyle O}{\|}}{C}-OH$

or H_3O^+

Carbonate ions react with water according to this equation:

$$CO_3^= + H_2O \rightleftharpoons HCO_3^- + OH^-$$

The conjugate base of HCO_3^- is _____.

$CO_3^=$

The conjugate acid of OH^- is _____.

H_2O

If you did the last few frames correctly, you know how to recognize acids and bases. The next section will discuss the reactions between them.

3.4 Neutralization: the formation of salts

When solutions of strong acids and bases are mixed together, a vigorous exothermic reaction ensues. Since water is only slightly dissociated into H^+ and OH^- ions, we would expect the two ions to combine readily to form H_2O molecules. The reaction is called *neutralization*. It is characteristic of acids and bases. In fact, their ability to neutralize one another's properties is often included in the definition of acids and bases.

The reaction between hydrochloric acid and sodium hydroxide is often represented by the equation

$$HCl + NaOH \rightarrow NaCl + H_2O$$

Because both the acid and base are strong electrolytes, a better way to write the equation is

$$H^+ + Cl^- + Na^+ + OH^- \rightarrow Na^+ + Cl^- + H_2O$$

When the spectator ions, Na$^+$ and Cl$^-$, are removed from the equation, the net reaction is

$$H^+ + OH^- \rightarrow H_2O$$

Nitric acid, HNO$_3$, is a strong acid. In aqueous solution, it is completely dissociated into _____ and _____ ions.

H^+; NO_3^-

Potassium hydroxide, KOH, is a strong base. An aqueous solution of KOH contains _____ and _____ ions.

K^+; OH^-

When solutions of HNO$_3$ and KOH are mixed in appropriate amounts, they _____ each other.

neutralize

The *net* equation for the reaction is _____. K$^+$ and NO$_3^-$ are spectator ions, which do not take part in the reaction.

$H^+ + OH^- \rightarrow H_2O$

The net reaction, H$^+$ + OH$^-$ → H$_2$O, represents the neutralization of any _____ by any _____ _____.

strong acid; strong base

Weak acids and bases are only slightly dissociated into ions; the most abundant species in their solution is the undissociated _____ of the acid or base.

molecule

Acetic acid, HC$_2$H$_3$O$_2$, is a relatively weak acid. Only a few _____ and _____ ions are present in an acetic acid solution.

H^+ *(hydrogen)*; $C_2H_3O_2^-$ *(acetate)*

When acetic acid is neutralized by a base, the species that is neutralized is the _____ molecule itself.

acetic acid

For this reason the net equation for the neutralization of a weak acid (is/is not) _____ the same as for a strong acid and strong base.

is not

The net equation for the neutralization of acetic acid by a strong base is HC$_2$H$_3$O$_2$ + OH$^-$ → H$_2$O + _____.

$C_2H_3O_2^-$

Chemical equilibrium and solutions   128

If HA represents any weak acid, the net equation for its neutralization by a strong base is _____ _____.

$$HA + OH^- \rightarrow H_2O + A^-$$

Likewise, the net equation for the neutralization of a weak base by a strong acid must show the disappearance of _____.

the molecules of the weak base

The net reaction for the neutralization of the weak base MOH can be written _____ _____.

$$H^+ + MOH \rightarrow M^+ + H_2O$$

And, finally, the neutralization of the weak acid HA by the weak base MOH is represented by the equation _____ _____.

$$HA + MOH \rightarrow M^+ + A^- + H_2O$$

If the net equation for the neutralization of any strong-acid—strong-base pair is

$$H^+ + OH^- \rightarrow H_2O$$

the heat of reaction should be the same for all of them. The following thermochemical equations indicate the experimental proof of the last statement:

$$HCl + NaOH \rightarrow NaCl + H_2O + 13,800 \text{ cal}$$
$$HNO_3 + KOH \rightarrow KNO_3 + H_2O + 13,800 \text{ cal}$$
$$H_2SO_4 + 2NaOH \rightarrow Na_2SO_4 + 2H_2O + 27,600 \text{ cal}$$

We may conclude that the union of H^+ and OH^- to form H_2O is an exothermic reaction which liberates $13,800$ cal for each mole of water formed. When weak acids or bases are involved, less heat is liberated because some of the energy is used to complete the dissociation of the weak electrolyte.

$Ba(OH)_2$ and HBr are strong electrolytes. How many calories are liberated when 1.00 mole of the base is neutralized by the acid? (*Hint:* Write the balanced equation for the reaction first.)

27,600 cal	Go to A below
13,800 cal	Go to B below
Insufficient information given	Go to C below

A

You are right. The thermochemical equation for the reaction is $Ba(OH)_2$ + $2HBr \rightarrow BaBr_2 + 2H_2O$ + 27,600 cal. Go to the paragraph following C below.

B

You are incorrect. Did you write a balanced equation for the reaction? Let's do it again to be sure you have it right. The reactants are $Ba(OH)_2$ and HBr. One of the products is water, and the other is $BaBr_2$. So we can write

$$Ba(OH)_2 + HBr \rightarrow H_2O + BaBr_2$$

But this isn't balanced, is it? It can be balanced easily by adding the coefficient 2 for HBr and H_2O.

$$Ba(OH)_2 + 2HBr \rightarrow 2H_2O + BaBr_2$$

The foregoing discussion pointed out that 13,800 cal is liberated for each mole of water formed in the neutralization of a strong acid and strong base. In this instance, 2.00 moles of water is formed when 1.00 mole of $Ba(OH)_2$ is neutralized. So 27,600 cal is liberated. Continue to the paragraph after C below.

C

You are wrong. What additional information do you want? The problem concerns the neutralization of the base $Ba(OH)_2$ by the acid HBr. The balanced equation for the reaction is

$$Ba(OH)_2 + 2HBr \rightarrow 2H_2O + BaBr_2$$

Read the discussion again and choose another answer.

The neutralization of an acid and base produces water and a third kind of substance known as a salt. Salts contain the positive cation of the base and the negative anion of the acid. A good definition of a salt is that it is the product of the neutralization of an acid and base.

When solutions of HCl and KOH are mixed, H_2O is produced, and the ions _____ and _____ remain in the solution.

Cl^-; K^+

If the water is evaporated, K^+ and Cl^- agglomerate to form the salt _____.

KCl

The net equation for the formation of the salt might be written _____ + _____ $\rightarrow$ KCl(s).

K^+; Cl^-

The salt that results from the neutralization of $Ba(OH)_2$ and HBr is _____.

$BaBr_2$ (*barium bromide*)

3.5 The ion product of water

In the discussion that preceded the section on acids and bases, you learned that pure water is an extremely weak electrolyte. The ions that conduct the electric current result from the dissociation of water into H^+ and OH^- as represented by the equation

$$H_2O \rightleftharpoons H^+ + OH^-$$

The dissociation is the reverse of the neutralization of strong acids and bases; it is an equilibrium reaction.

The equilibrium exists in pure water and in all aqueous solutions. It must satisfy the equilibrium condition

$$\frac{[H^+][OH^-]}{[H_2O]} = K$$

In pure water and in dilute aqueous solutions the concentration of H_2O may be regarded as constant and combined with K to give this expression

$$K[H_2O] = [H^+][OH^-] = K_w$$

Because it is used so frequently and is so important, the constant is designated K_w to distinguish it from other equilibrium constants.

K_w is called the *ion product of water*. In the 20 to 25°C temperature range it has the value 1.0×10^{-14}. It is impossible to overestimate the importance and usefulness of this constant.

In pure water, all H^+ and OH^- must result from the dissociation of _____ molecules.

H_2O (*water*)

For this reason, the concentrations of H^+ and OH^- in pure water are (equal/unequal) _____.

equal

If d represents the number of moles of H^+ produced per liter, _____ moles of OH^- are produced at the same time.

d

The ion-product expression becomes $K_w = [H^+][OH^-] = d^2 =$ _____.

1.0×10^{-14}

From this we can calculate that $[H^+] = [OH^-] = d =$
_____.

1.0×10^{-7}

Our working definition of an acid is that it increases the _____ concentration.

H^+ (*hydrogen-ion*)

At the same time there must be a _____ in the hydroxide-ion concentration.

decrease

Likewise, when $[OH^-]$ is increased by the addition of a base, _____ must decrease.

$[H^+]$

The vital point is that the relationship $K_w =$ _____ $= 1.0 \times 10^{-14}$ must hold true at all times in all aqueous solutions.

$[H^+][OH^-]$

A solution is found to have an H^+ concentration of 2.0×10^{-3} M. What is the OH^- concentration?

2.0×10^{-3} Go to A below
1.0×10^{-14} Go to B below
5.0×10^{-12} Go to C below

A

You are wrong. The OH^- concentration is not 2.0×10^{-3}. Let's look at the problem. The information given is that $[H^+] = 2.0 \times 10^{-3}$. The answer you've chosen says that

$$[H^+] = [OH^-] = 2.0 \times 10^{-3}$$

Didn't you just learn that these two concentrations are equal only in pure water and that the numerical value is 1.0×10^{-7}?

The relationship that holds for all aqueous solutions is

$$K_w = [H^+][OH^-] = 1.0 \times 10^{-14}$$

Substitute 2.0×10^{-3} for $[H^+]$ and solve for $[OH^-]$, Then go back and choose another answer.

B

Incorrect. The OH^- concentration is not 1.0×10^{-14}. The information given is that $[H^+] = 2.0 \times 10^{-3}$. You have just learned a relationship that holds true for all aqueous solutions. (If you haven't, learn it now.)

$$K_w = [H^+][OH^-] = 1.0 \times 10^{-14}$$

Substitute 2.0×10^{-3} for $[H^+]$ and solve for $[OH^-]$. Then turn back and choose another answer.

C

Correct.

$$[OH^-] = \frac{K_w}{[H^+]} = \frac{1.0 \times 10^{-14}}{2.0 \times 10^{-3}} = 5.0 \times 10^{-12}$$

By now you should be able to identify most acids, bases, and salts when you see their formulas. As your experience in chemistry increases, so will your skill in identifying them.

For example, H_3PO_4 is a(n) _____.   *acid*

$NaCl$ is a(n) _____.   *salt*

K_3PO_4 is a(n) _____.   *salt*

$Ca(OH)_2$ is a(n) _____.   *base*

$HC_2H_3O_2$ and $HCHO_2$ are _____.   *acids*

Strong acids are _____ dis-   *highly* or *almost*
sociated in aqueous solution.   *completely*

Weak acids are _____ dissociated than   *much less*
strong acids.

H_2SO_4, HNO_3, and HCl are (strong/weak) _____   *strong*
_____ acids.

HF, HCN, and $HC_2H_3O_2$ are common (strong/weak)
_____ acids.   *weak*

The only common weak base you will encounter is NH_3.
Its name is _____.   *ammonia*

3.6 pH and pOH

The hydrogen-ion concentration is an important factor in many reactions that take place in solution, particularly biological reactions. To simplify the expression of small concentrations, a unit known as pH has been developed. It is defined as the negative logarithm of the hydrogen-ion concentration.

$$pH = - \log [H^+] = \log \frac{1}{[H^+]} \qquad or \qquad [H^+] = 10^{-pH}$$

As usual, $[H^+]$ signifies the hydrogen-ion concentration in moles per liter of solution.
    Once you have the definition of pH clearly in mind, the calculation of pH becomes strictly a mathematical exercise. Here is a typical problem. Follow its solution carefully.

Problem: What is the pH of a solution in which $[H^+] = 0.0025\ M$?
Solution: By definition, $pH = - \log [H^+] = - \log 0.0025$.
Then, since

$$\log 0.0025 = 7.40 - 10$$
$$- \log 0.0025 = -(7.40 - 10) = -(-2.60)$$

and

$$pH = 2.60$$

Note that the characteristic (number to the left of the decimal point) of a logarithm may be positive or negative. The mantissa (number to the right of the decimal point) is always positive.

Are you ready to try a problem on your own? Good.

What is the pH of a solution for which $[H^+] = 0.04$ M?

1.4   Go to A below
1.6   Go to B below
2.4   Go to C below

A

You are right. When $[H^+] = 0.04$ M, pH $= 1.4$. The steps in solving the problem are:

$$
\begin{aligned}
pH &= - \log 0.04 \\
&= -(8.6 - 10) \\
&= -(-1.4) \\
&= 1.4
\end{aligned}
$$

Go on to the paragraph following C.

B

You are incorrect. You probably made a mistake in your algebra. When

$$[H^+] = 0.04 \ M$$

the pH is not 1.6. The steps in solving the problem are:

$$
\begin{aligned}
pH &= - \log 0.04 \\
&= -(8.6 - 10) \\
&= -(-1.4) \\
&= 1.4
\end{aligned}
$$

When you look up 4 on a logarithm table, you find 60. This part of the logarithm is positive. The characteristic of the logarithm of 0.04, however, is -2. The characteristic may also be written as $8 - 10$. Thus the logarithm of 0.04 is $8.6 - 10$. Go on to the paragraph following C.

C

Wrong. It appears that you made a mistake in your arithmetic. The first step in solving the problem is to apply the definition of pH:

$$pH = - \log [H^+]$$

From this it follows that $pH = - \log 0.04$ and $pH = -(8.6 - 10)$. Simplify the right side of the last equation carefully, and you should get an answer different from 2.4. Go back and see if it's one of the choices.

Because $[H^+]$ often has extremely small values, the use of exponents is a great time-saver. For instance, $[H^+] = 0.000042$ becomes $[H^+] = 4.2 \times 10^{-5}$. Check your knowledge of exponents on these sample problems.

$[H^+] = 0.40 = $ _____ . 4.0×10^{-1}

$[H^+] = 0.0025 = $ _____ . 2.5×10^{-3}

$[H^+] = 1.2 = $ _____ . 1.2×10^{0}

If you had no difficulty with these exercises, skip to page 138. If you wish to review exponents, go right on.

Movement of the decimal point in a number is just an easy way of multiplying or dividing it by powers of 10. So the first thing you must master is the use of exponents to express numbers as powers of 10. This table should make it clear to you.

Decimal number	Exponential number
10	10^1
100	10^2
1,000	10^3
1	10^0
0.1	10^{-1}
0.01	10^{-2}
0.001	10^{-3}

As an example, let's take the number 4.00 and move the decimal point.

Number	Decimal-point movement	New number	= Exponential number
4.00	1 place right	40.0	= 4.00×10^1
4.00	2 places right	400.	= 4.00×10^2
4.00	3 places right	4,000.	= 4.00×10^3
4.00	1 place left	0.400	= 4.00×10^{-1}
4.00	2 places left	0.0400	= 4.00×10^{-2}
4.00	3 places left	0.00400	= 4.00×10^{-3}

From this table you can generalize to state two rules. They are:

Rule 1: Moving the decimal point in a number to the right *multiplies* the number by 10 for each place it is moved.

Rule 2: Moving the decimal point in a number to the left *divides* the number by 10 for each place it is moved.

Now we're ready to tackle the three examples which troubled you. The principle involved is that we want to move the decimal point without changing the magnitude of the number. This is done by the clever device of multiplying *and* dividing the number by the same factor.

The first example is

$$0.40 = 4.0 \times 10^{-1}$$

The decimal point was moved one place to the right. This multiplied the number by 10. The division by 10 was accomplished through multiplication by 0.1, or 10^{-1}.

The second example is

$$0.0025 = 2.5 \times 10^{-3}$$

The decimal point was moved three places to the right. This action multiplied the number by 1,000. Division by 1,000 was done through multiplication by 0.001, or 10^{-3}.

The final example is

$$1.2 = 1.2 \times 10^0$$

The decimal point isn't moved. The 10^0 was added to ensure that you understand $1 = 10^0$.

Finally, check these additional examples:

$37.2 = $ _____ $\times 10^1$ 3.72

$0.94 = 9.4 \times$ _____ 10^{-1}

$0.00076 = 7.6 \times$ _____ 10^{-4}

$396,000 = $ _____ $\times 10^4$ 39.6

If you're still not confident of your ability to handle exponents, you should ask your instructor or a classmate for additional help. If you are confident, go on.

The calculation of pH is simpler when $[H^+]$ is expressed in exponential terms. The characteristic of log $[H^+]$ is the exponent of 10. Check yourself on these two sample problems.

Problem: What is the pH of a solution for which $[H^+] = 0.40$?
Solution: $[H^+] = 4.0 \times 10^{-1}$

$$pH = - \log (4.0 \times 10^{-1})$$
$$= -(0.6 - 1)$$
$$= 0.4$$

Problem: What is the pH of a solution if $[H^+] = 4.2 \times 10^{-5}$?
Solution:

$$pH = - \log (4.2 \times 10^{-5})$$
$$= -(0.62 - 5)$$
$$= -(-4.38)$$
$$= 4.38$$

You can see that you need to be careful with your algebra and logarithms to avoid errors. Accuracy and facility result from conscientious practice.

The hydrogen-ion concentration of a solution is $7.5 \times 10^{-7}\ M$. Calculate the pH.

6.12   Go to A below
6.88   Go to B below
7.12   Go to C below
7.88   Go to D below

A

You are correct. The pH is 6.12. The solution is summarized by the equation $pH = -\log (7.5 \times 10^{-7}) = -(0.88 - 7) = -(-6.12) = 6.12$. Go to the paragraph following D.

B, C, D

Incorrect. You seem to be having some trouble with your algebra and logarithms. A good idea with problems of this sort is first to find the outside limits of the answer and then to zero in on it. This little table shows you how.

$[H^+]$		pH
10×10^{-7} or 1×10^{-6}		6.0
7.5×10^{-7}		?
1×10^{-7}		7.0

You can figure the pH's for the even powers of 10 in your head. In this instance you can see that the pH must be between 6.0 and 7.0. Follow this example very closely to see if you can discover your error.

Problem: $[H^+] = 2.5 \times 10^{-4}$. What is the pH?
Solution: By definition,

$$pH = -\log [H^+] = -\log (2.5 \times 10^{-4})$$

That ends the chemistry. The rest is math. The problem is to simplify the logarithm into an ordinary number. Let's do it. As you can see, 2.5×10^{-4} is a product of two numbers. You know that the logarithm of such a product is the sum of the logarithms of the individual numbers. So,

$$-\log (2.5 \times 10^{-4}) = -(\log 2.5 + \log 10^{-4})$$

Taking the logarithms,

$$- \log (2.5 \times 10^{-4}) = -[0.40 + (-4)]$$

Removing the parentheses first,

$$- \log (2.5 \times 10^{-4}) = -[0.40 - 4]$$

Subtracting within the brackets,

$$- \log (2.5 \times 10^{-4}) = -[-3.60]$$

And finally removing the brackets,

$$- \log (2.5 \times 10^{-4}) = pH = 3.60$$

That's all there is to it. Since you will be called on often to calculate pH's, you should learn the steps so well that they become nearly instinctive. Now go back and rework the original problem again.

You now have a mastery of the steps involved in calculating the pH of a solution if you know the hydrogen-ion concentration. Since there are electrical instruments that measure pH directly, it is also necessary that you be able to calculate the hydrogen-ion concentration that corresponds to a given pH value.

Problem: The pH of a solution is 3.7. What is $[H^+]$?
Solution: By definition,

$$pH = 3.7 = - \log [H^+]$$

Multiplying both sides of the equation by -1,

$$-3.7 = \log [H^+]$$

As you know, every logarithm must have a positive mantissa. Therefore, -3.7 must be changed into the sum of a negative number and a positive number. This can be done as follows:

$$-3.7 = (-4) + (0.3) = \log [H^+]$$

The logarithm of the hydrogen-ion concentration is now known to be the sum of two logarithms. The concentration itself is a product of two numbers. Taking antilogarithms,

$$\text{antilog}\,[(-4) + (0.3)] = (10^{-4})(2) = [H^+]$$

which can be rearranged to

$$[H^+] = 2 \times 10^{-4}$$

Now you try one by yourself.

What is the $[H^+]$ of a solution whose pH is 9.60?

2.5×10^{-9}	Go to A below
4.0×10^{-9}	Go to B below
2.5×10^{-10}	Go to C below

A and B

Incorrect. If you have difficulty with this type of pH problem, it may help you to establish some limits within which the answer must fall. This can be done as shown in this table.

pH	$[H^+]$
9.0	$10 \times 10^{-10}\ (1 \times 10^{-9})$
9.60	?
10.0	1×10^{-10}

You should be able to figure the hydrogen-ion concentrations that correspond to the whole number pH's mentally. Now you can see that the answer to this problem must be between 1×10^{-10} and 10×10^{-10}. Go back and rework the problem.

C

Right. The hydrogen-ion concentration is 2.5×10^{-10}. The steps in the solution of the problem are

$$9.60 = -\log [H^+] = (0.40) + (-10)$$
$$[H^+] = \text{antilog}\,[(0.40) + (-10)] = 2.5 \times 10^{-10}$$

There is a unit for expressing [OH⁻] which is exactly analogous to pH. As you may have guessed already, it is called pOH. By definition,

$$pOH = -\log [OH^-] = \log \frac{1}{[OH^-]}$$

or $[OH^-] = 10^{-pOH}$

All the foregoing statements about pH apply to pOH as well. This little pOH problem should be easy for you to solve.

Calculate the pOH of an aqueous solution which has $[OH^-] = 3.0 \times 10^{-2}$.

1.48   Go to A below
1.52   Go to B below
2.48   Go to C below
2.52   Go to D below

A

Incorrect. The pOH is not 1.48. You probably were a bit careless with your algebra. Check your calculations and choose another answer.

B

You are correct. The pOH is 1.52. The steps in the solution of the problem are

$$pOH = -\log (3.0 \times 10^{-2})$$
$$= -(0.48 - 2)$$
$$= -(-1.52) = 1.52$$

Go on to the paragraph following D.

C and D

You are wrong. You seem to be having some difficulty with logarithms. Remember that pH and pOH are quite similar. It is a good idea to establish some limits within which your answer must fall. Here is one way to do it.

[OH$^-$]	pOH
1.0 × 10^{-2}	2.0
3.0 × 10^{-2}	?
10.0 × 10^{-2} (1 × 10^{-1})	1.0

It is apparent that the answer you are seeking must lie between 1.0 and 2.0. Go back and calculate the answer again.

You will remember that the equilibrium condition for the dissociation of pure water establishes a definite relationship between [H$^+$] and [OH$^-$]. It is expressed by the equation

$$K_w = [\text{H}^+][\text{OH}^-] = 1.0 \times 10^{-14} \quad \text{at 20 to 25°C}$$

This can be combined with the definitions of pH and pOH to derive a useful relationship between pH and pOH. Let's start with the ion-product equation.

$$[\text{H}^+][\text{OH}^-] = 1.0 \times 10^{-14}$$

Take the logarithm of all terms:

$$\log[\text{H}^+] + \log[\text{OH}^-] = -14$$

Multiply all terms by -1:

$$-\log[\text{H}^+] + (-\log[\text{OH}^-]) = 14$$

Substitute pH $= -\log[\text{H}^+]$ and pOH $= -\log[\text{OH}^-]$:

$$\text{pH} + \text{pOH} = 14$$

If you know these two relationships, you can calculate any one of the four quantities [H$^+$], [OH$^-$], pH, and pOH from any one of the others. You will often be asked to do so—starting now.

In an aqueous solution, if [H$^+$] = 4.0 × 10^{-6}, [OH$^-$] = _____.

$$\frac{1 \times 10^{-14}}{4.0 \times 10^{-6}}$$
$$= 2.5 \times 10^{-9}$$

In the same solution, if [OH$^-$] = 2.5 × 10^{-9}, pOH = _____.

8.60

If the pOH of the solution is 8.60, pH = _____. 5.40

For another aqueous solution, $[H^+] = 1.0 \times 10^{-8}$; pOH

= _____. 6.0

In pure water, $[H^+] = 1.0 \times 10^{-7}$. The pH of pure
water is _____. 7.0

If the pH of pure water is 7.0, its pOH is _____. 7.0

By definition, a neutral solution has equal $[H^+]$ and
$[OH^-]$. The pH of a neutral solution is _____. The pOH 7.0
of a neutral solution is _____. 7.0

An acidic solution is one in which $[H^+]$ is (less than/
equal to/greater than) _____ $[OH^-]$. *greater than*

The pH of an acidic solution is (less than/equal to/
greater than) _____ 7.0. *less than*

The pH of a basic solution is (less than/equal to/greater
than) _____ 7.0. *greater than*

So far this discussion of pH and pOH has been little more than an exercise in
the application of algebra to some rather simple definitions. Some of the practical
problems you will face require the application of chemical principles as well. Suppose you wish to calculate the pH of a 0.025 M solution of HCl. How would you
proceed?

By definition, pH = _____. $- log \ [H^+]$

To calculate the pH a numerical value for _____ $[H^+]$
is needed.

HCl is a strong acid. In water it dissociates completely
into _____ and _____ ions. H^+; Cl^-

Therefore, if the original solution contained 0.025 mole
of HCl/liter, $[H^+]$ = _____. 0.025

And the pH of the solution is _____. 1.60

The hydrogen-ion concentration for solutions of all strong acids may be determined in this manner. The situation with respect to weak acids is more complicated and is beyond the scope of this discussion.

$Ba(OH)_2$ is a strong base that dissociates in water as shown by this equation

$$Ba(OH)_2 \rightarrow Ba^{++} + 2\ OH^-$$

What is the pOH of a 0.0005 M solution of $Ba(OH)_2$?

3.0	Go to A below
3.3	Go to B below
3.7	Go to C below
4.0	Go to D below

A

Right. The pOH of a 0.0005 M solution of $Ba(OH)_2$ is 3.0. The hydroxide-ion concentration is $2 \times 0.0005 = 0.001\ M$. By inspection, pOH = 3.0. Continue to the paragraph following D.

B

Incorrect. The pOH is not 3.3. You have not taken into account the fact that 1 mole of $Ba(OH)_2$ produces 2 moles of OH^- ions when it dissociates. Go back and try again.

C

You are wrong. The pOH is not 3.7. You seem to have made two errors, one in chemistry and one in algebra. The first is that you have not taken into account the fact that 1 mole of $Ba(OH)_2$ produces 2 moles of OH^- when it dissociates. Second, you are still unsure in your use of logarithms. Perhaps you should turn back to pages 134–138 for a quick review. In any event, go back and calculate another answer.

D

Incorrect. The pOH is not 4.0. You seem to have recognized that 1 mole of $Ba(OH)_2$ produces 2 moles of OH^- ions when it dissociates. You did not, however, arrive at the right answer. You may well have made an arithmetical error. Turn back, read the problem carefully, and work out another answer.

Many students believe that pH and pOH values range only between 0 and 14. The falsity of this belief can easily be seen if you calculate the pH and pOH of a concentrated, 12 M HCl solution.

If the solution is 12 M, then [H$^+$] = 12 because HCl is a strong acid.

$$\text{pH} = -\log(12) = -\log(1.2 \times 10^1) = -(0.08 + 1) = -1.08$$
$$\text{pOH} = 14.0 - \text{pH} = 14.0 - (-1.08) = 15.08$$

You should now be ready for some drill problems on pH and pOH. They can all be solved readily if you keep three facts in mind. They are:

1. Strong acids and bases dissociate completely in water.
2. pH = $-\log$ [H$^+$] and pOH = $-\log$ [OH$^-$].
3. K_w = [H$^+$][OH$^-$] = 1.0×10^{-14} at 20 to 25°C.

Hydrobromic acid, HBr, is a strong acid. The hydrogen-ion concentration of 0.50 M HBr is _____ M.	0.50
The pH of the solution is _____.	0.30
The pOH of the solution is _____, and [OH$^-$] = _____.	13.70 2×10^{-14}
A solution is reported to have a pOH of 3.6. The pH of the solution is _____. The solution is (acidic/basic) _____.	10.4 *basic*
The pH of a 0.00537 M solution of HCl is _____.	2.27
The pOH of a 2.24×10^{-4} M solution of NaOH is _____. Its pH is _____.	3.65; 10.35

3.7 Titrations: the arithmetic of reactions in solution

Chemists frequently wish to measure the amount of acid or base in a sample of material. These measurements are usually made with solutions. The use of solutions as a source of reactants is convenient because different amounts of reactant can be measured out by taking different volumes of a solution of known concentration. As an example, suppose you want to determine the amount of HCl in a particular solution. You can do it if you have a solution of a base with a known concentration.

You have already learned that acids and bases neutralize one another. In such a neutralization it is essential that equal numbers of H^+ and OH^- ions be available for the reaction. For the present let's assume that you intend to neutralize the HCl with NaOH. The non-net equation for the reaction is

$$HCl + NaOH \rightarrow H_2O + NaCl$$

According to the equation, complete neutralization of 1 mole of HCl will require _____ mole(s) of NaOH.

1

Neutralization of 0.47 mole of HCl will require _____ mole(s) of NaOH.

0.47

The neutralization of any number of HCl requires _____ number of moles of NaOH.

the same or *an equal*

The procedure for carrying out reactions in solutions and measuring the amounts of reactants is called *titration*. A titration is the progressive addition of small quantities of one reactant to a given amount of the other reactant. For your titration of HCl with NaOH, a carefully measured volume of the HCl solution might be placed in a beaker or conical flask. The NaOH solution, whose concentration is already known, can be added from a burette. Let's do a mental titration.

First, in your mind's eye, carefully measure out exactly 25.00 ml of the HCl solution into a beaker. Fill your burette with the exactly 0.100 M NaOH solution that you just happen to have.

Before any of the NaOH is added, the beaker contains only the HCl solution. There is an excess of _____ ions.

H^+

As portions of the NaOH solution are added, the H^+ and OH^- neutralize each other, and the concentration of H^+ becomes _____.

smaller

Because the expression $[H^+][OH^-] = 1.0 \times 10^{-14}$ must be satisfied, the concentration of OH^- becomes _____ _____ at the same time.

larger

Finally, a point can be reached where [H$^+$] = [OH$^-$]. The solution is neither acidic nor basic, but _____ _____.

neutral

At the neutral point, the number of moles of NaOH is exactly equal to _____ of HCl in the original 25-ml sample.

the number of moles

Looking at the burette, you find that 20.0 ml of NaOH was required to reach the neutral point. The number of moles of NaOH used is _____.

(.020 *liter*)
× (0.100 *mole/liter*)
= 0.0020

The 25.0-ml sample of HCl contained _____ mole(s) of HCl.

0.0020

The concentration of the HCl solution was _____ _____ M.

$\dfrac{0.0020\ mole}{0.025\ liter}$
= 0.080

That's easy, isn't it? One problem, however, remains to be solved. Do you know what it is? It's "How do we recognize the neutral point?" The neutral point is found by means of an *indicator*. An indicator is anything that undergoes an observable change at the neutral point. Although an electrical property of the solution may be used, most acid-base indicators are organic compounds that have one color in an acidic solution and another color in a basic solution. A single drop of excess acid or base is enough to change the color of a good indicator such as litmus, methyl red, or phenolphthalein.

Your next titration involves the neutralization of 35.0 ml of a KOH solution with 0.140 M HNO$_3$. You reach the neutral point when 50.0 ml have been added. What is the molarity of the KOH?

0.0980 M Go to A below
0.140 M Go to B below
0.200 M Go to C below
Help!   Go to D below

A

Incorrect. You may have made an inadvertent error. To avoid such errors you should always test your answers to be sure that they are reasonable. In this situation you know that 35.0 ml of the KOH solution contains the same number of moles as 50.0 ml of 0.140 M HNO_3. Doesn't it stand to reason that the molarity of the KOH solution is greater than the HNO_3? Go back and work the problem again.

B

You are wrong. Although $[H^+] = [OH^-]$ at the neutral point, the molarity of the acid does not necessarily equal the molarity of the base. In the present situation you know that 35.0 ml of the KOH solution contains the same number of moles as 50.0 ml of 0.140 M HNO_3. Isn't it reasonable that the molarity of the KOH solution is greater than that of the HNO_3? Work the problem again and choose another answer.

C

You are right. The KOH solution is 0.200 M. The calculation is summarized by this equation

$$\frac{(0.140 \text{ mole } HNO_3/\text{liter})(0.050 \text{ liter } HNO_3)}{(0.0350 \text{ liter KOH})} = 0.0200 \ M$$

Go to the paragraph following D.

D

First, let's look at the non-net equation for the reaction. It is $HNO_3 + KOH \rightarrow H_2O + KNO_3$. Since the acid and base react in a $1:1$ ratio, the number of moles of HNO_3 and KOH must be equal at the neutral point. You can find the number of moles of HNO_3 from the volume and molarity that are given.

$$\text{moles } HNO_3 = (0.140 \text{ mole/liter})(0.050 \text{ liter}) = 0.00700$$

This number of moles is contained in 35.0 ml (0.0350 liter) of KOH. Can you find its molarity now? If so, do it and turn back to choose another answer. If not, go back and review the work you did on your first titration.

Suppose you mix a large volume of a solution of a base with a large volume of a solution of an acid. Is there a way to tell whether the final solution will be acidic, basic, or neutral? Yes. Let's look at an example.

Problem: When 250 ml of 0.20 M NaOH is mixed with 750 ml of 0.10 M HCl, is the resulting mixture acidic, basic, or neutral?

First, let's find the number of moles of acid and base. In 250 ml of 0.20 M NaOH, there is _____ _____ mole of base.

$(0.20\ M)(0.25\ liter)$
$= 0.050$

Likewise, 750 ml of 0.10 M HCl contains _____ _____ mole of acid.

$(0.10\ M)(0.750\ liter)$
$= 0.075$

Since 1 mole of NaOH will neutralize _____ mole of HCl, there is an excess of _____.

1
HCl

The number of moles of excess HCl is _____ _____.

$0.075 - 0.050$
$= 0.025$

If we assume that the final volume of solution is 1,000 ml $(250 + 750)$, the mixture contains 0.025 mole of excess HCl per liter. The solution is (acidic/basic/neutral) _____.

acidic

Because HCl dissociates completely, [H$^+$] = _____.

0.025

Try your hand at this problem of the same kind.

When 100 ml of 0.250 M HNO$_3$ and 400 ml of 0.100 M KOH is mixed together, the resulting solution is equivalent to (assume final volume is 500 ml):

0.015 M HNO$_3$ Go to A below
0.030 M HNO$_3$ Go to B below
0.015 M KOH   Go to C below
0.030 M KOH   Go to D below

A and B

Incorrect. Are you sure the solution is acidic? Let's check.

$$(0.100 \text{ liter})(0.025 \ M \ \text{HNO}_3) = 0.025 \text{ mole HNO}_3$$
$$(0.400 \text{ liter})(0.100 \ M \ \text{KOH}) = 0.040 \text{ mole KOH}$$

There's more KOH, isn't there? How much more? And in what volume? When you have it figured out, go back and choose another answer.

C

Almost right. The solution is basic. There's an excess of 0.015 mole of KOH. But what is the volume of the mixture? It's only 0.500 liter. What's the molarity?

$$\frac{0.015 \text{ mole KOH}}{0.500 \text{ liter}} = 0.030 \ M \ \text{KOH}$$

Go on to the paragraph after D.

D

You are correct. The mixture is equivalent to a solution of 0.030 M KOH. There is an excess of 0.015 mole of KOH in 0.500 liter. Go on to the next paragraph.

Although H^+ and OH^- ions always react in a ratio of 1 mole to 1 mole in any neutralization reaction, the same cannot be said for the acids and bases themselves. For instance, the non-net equation for the complete neutralization of $Ba(OH)_2$ by H_3PO_4 is

$$3Ba(OH)_2 + 2H_3PO_4 \rightarrow Ba_3(PO_4)_2 + 6H_2O$$

Each mole of $Ba(OH)_2$ furnishes 2 moles of OH^-. Each mole of H_3PO_4 supplies 3 moles of H^+. The acid and base neutralize each other completely when 3 moles of base have reacted with 2 moles of the acid.

3.8 Gram-equivalents of acids and bases; normality of solutions

Because various acids and bases dissociate to give different numbers of H^+ and OH^- ions, chemists find it convenient to focus their attention on the hydrogen and hydroxide ions themselves. A new term, the *gram-equivalent*, is our tool for this purpose.

One gram-equivalent of an acid is the weight required to supply 1 mole of H^+. Likewise, 1 gram-equivalent of base is the weight required to supply 1 mole of OH^-. It follows from these definitions, then, that 1 g-equiv of any acid exactly neutralizes 1 g-equiv of any base.

Nitric acid, HNO_3, is one of the simplest acids. 1 mole of HNO_3 can supply ————— mole of H^+. 　　　　　　1

Therefore, 1 mole of HNO_3 is ——— g-equiv of HNO_3. 　　　　1

The formula weight of HNO_3 is 63.0. 1 mole of HNO_3 weighs ——— g. 1 g-equiv of HNO_3 weighs ——— g. 　　63.0; 63.0

A similar situation prevails for bases. 1 mole of KOH is also ————— g-equiv. 　　　　1

The number of gram-equivalents of NaOH required to neutralize 1.5 g-equiv of HCl is —————. 　　　　1.5

By now you're probably asking "Why bring in this business about gram-equivalents? Aren't they the same as moles?" For acids that supply only 1 mole of hydrogen ions per mole of acid, the mole and the gram-equivalent are the same. They are identical also for bases that supply 1 mole of hydroxide ions per mole of base.

But what about an acid like H_2SO_4 or a base such as $Ba(OH)_2$? A mole of H_2SO_4 can react with NaOH according to this equation

$$H_2SO_4 + 2NaOH \rightarrow Na_2SO_4 + 2H_2O$$

As you can see, 1 mole of H_2SO_4 supplies 2 moles of H^+ in the reaction. Therefore, 1 mole of H_2SO_4 is 2 g-equiv. The weight of 1 g-equiv is $\frac{1}{2}$ the weight of 1 mole, or $\frac{1}{2}$ the formula weight. Another route to the same conclusion is to consider that 1 mole of H_2SO_4 reacts with 2 g-equiv of NaOH.

The entire argument can be reduced to a simple equation:

$$\text{g-equiv wt} = \frac{\text{formula wt}}{x}$$

where $x =$ for acids, the number of hydrogen ions per mole provided for reaction; for bases, the number of hydroxide ions per mole provided for reaction.

For the chemical reaction between H_2SO_4 and NaOH shown above, x for the acid is _____.

2

The formula weight of H_2SO_4 is 98. The gram-equivalent weight is _____.

49

For the base NaOH, $x =$ _____ and the gram-equivalent weight is _____.

1
40

Sulfuric acid and sodium hydroxide can also react to produce water and sodium hydrogen sulfate, as shown by this equation:

$$H_2SO_4 + NaOH \rightarrow NaHSO_4 + H_2O$$

In this reaction, each mole of H_2SO_4 provides _____ mole(s) of hydrogen ion.

1

For H_2SO_4, $x =$ _____, and the gram-equivalent weight is _____.

1
98

For NaOH, $x =$ _____, and the gram-equivalent weight is _____.

1
40

Obviously, the gram-equivalent weight of a substance depends on the reaction in which it takes part. The weight of a mole of a substance does not change; the weight of a gram-equivalent may.

1 mole of H_2SO_4 always weighs _____ g.

98

1 g-equiv of H_2SO_4 may weigh _____ g or _____ g.

98; 49

Whether the gram-equivalent weight of H_2SO_4 is 98 or 49 g depends on _____.

the chemical reaction

Calcium hydroxide and hydrochloric acid may react as shown by this equation

$$Ca(OH)_2 + HCl \rightarrow H_2O + CaCl_2$$

As written here, the equation (is/is not) _____ balanced.

is not

Still, from an inspection of the unbalanced equation, one
can see that each mole of $Ca(OH)_2$ provides _____
mole(s) of OH^- and each mole of HCl provides _____
mole(s) of H^+.

2

1

The formula weight of $Ca(OH)_2$ is 74. For this reaction
its gram-equivalent weight is _____ g.

37

You will probably be faced with problems that require you to calculate or
determine the gram-equivalent weight of a substance without any statement con-
cerning the reaction. In such instances, it is customary to assume that the acid or
base is to be completely neutralized. Therefore, the answer to the question "What
is the gram-equivalent weight of H_2SO_4?" is 49 g.
The next few frames will help you to consolidate your understanding of the
concept of gram-equivalents. After you have done them, we'll put the idea to use.

The formula weight of HCl is 36.5. The gram-equivalent weight of HCl is _____ g.

36.5

1 mole of HCl weighs _____ g.

36.5

The formula weight of NaOH is 40. The gram-equivalent weight of NaOH is _____ g.

40

The weight of 0.20 g-equiv of NaOH is _____ g.

8.0

Phosphoric acid, H_3PO_4, has a formula weight of 98.0.
If it is completely neutralized, its gram-equivalent
weight is _____ g.

32.7

When it reacts with KOH, H_3PO_4 can form the salts
KH_2PO_4, K_2HPO_4, or K_3PO_4. If K_2HPO_4 is the product, the gram-equivalent weight of H_3PO_4 is _____ g.

49.0

Regardless of the salt produced, the gram-equivalent
weight of KOH is _____ g.

56.1

The formula weight of $Ca(OH)_2$ is 74. The gram-equivalent weight of $Ca(OH)_2$ is _____ g.

37

If a flask contains 5.2 g of $Ca(OH)_2$, it contains
_____ g-equiv.

0.14

If this 5.2 g of $Ca(OH)_2$ is dissolved in enough water to make 0.50 liter of solution, the concentration of the solution is _____ g-equiv/liter.

0.28

When the solution is diluted to a volume of 1.0 liter, the concentration is _____ g-equiv $Ca(OH)_2$/liter.

0.14

The idea of gram-equivalents is needed for you to understand a new means of expressing the concentration of solutions. It is *normality*. The normality of a solution is the number of gram-equivalents of solute per liter of solution. You should recognize the resemblance to *molarity*, the number of moles of solute per liter of solution. Comparison of the basic equations makes it even more striking.

$$\text{Normality } (N) = \frac{\text{g-equiv of solute}}{\text{vol in liters}}$$

$$= \frac{\text{wt of solute/g-equiv wt}}{\text{vol in liters}}$$

$$\text{Molarity } (M) = \frac{\text{moles of solute}}{\text{vol in liters}}$$

$$= \frac{\text{wt of solute/formula wt}}{\text{vol in liters}}$$

The only difference is the use of the gram-equivalent weight in place of the formula weight. You have just learned the relationship between the two. It is

$$\text{g-equiv wt} = \frac{\text{formula wt}}{x}$$

By means of a little bit of algebraic hocus-pocus, it is possible to derive a relationship between molarity and normality. Can you do it?

$N = \dfrac{M}{x}$ Go to A below

$N = (M)(x)$ Go to B below

$N = M$ Go to C below

A

Incorrect. You may have made a careless mistake in your algebra. Whatever your error, let's look at the situation closely.

The only difference in the basic equations for normality and molarity, which were given above, is that gram-equivalent weight appears in one and formula weight appears in the other. You know that

$$\text{g-equiv wt} = \frac{\text{formula wt}}{x}$$

Let's substitute this into the basic equation for normality.

$$N = \frac{\text{wt of solute}/(\text{formula wt}/x)}{\text{vol in liters}}$$

You also know that

$$M = \frac{\text{wt of solute}/\text{formula wt}}{\text{vol in liters}}$$

The last step is to factor Eq. (1) in such a way that you can introduce M from Eq. (2). When you have done this, go back and choose another answer.

B

You are right. The relationship is $N = (M)(x)$. This is a valuable piece of knowledge. You will frequently need to convert normality to molarity and vice versa. Continue to the paragraph following C.

C

Wrong. $N = M$ only when the gram-equivalent weight and the formula weight of a solute are equal. The answer you want must hold true for all situations. Try to factor the basic equation for N so that you can introduce the equation for M into it. Then choose another answer.

Molarity and normality are both subject to the disadvantage that they change slightly as the density of solutions changes with temperature. Still they are the most common expressions of concentration. The step-by-step solution of a couple of typical problems should be enough to clarify the calculation of normality.

Problem: Calculate the normality of a solution which contains 15.2 g of H_2SO_4 in 500.0 ml of solution.

The formula weight of H_2SO_4 is 98.1. The gram-equivalent weight is _____ g.

49.0

The number of gram-equivalents in 15.2 g is _____.

$$\frac{15.2\ g}{49.0\ g/g\text{-}equiv} = 0.310$$

Since the volume is 0.500 liter, N = _____.

$$\frac{0.310\ g\text{-}equiv}{0.500\ liter} = 0.620$$

Problem: What is the molarity of a 0.620 N solution of H_2SO_4?

Because $x = 2$, M = _____.

0.310

According to our definition, an acid is any substance that increases the hydrogen-ion concentration of water. Some solutes react with the solvent to produce an acid. The normality can be determined in the usual manner.

When sulfur trioxide, SO_3, dissolves in water, a solution of sulfuric acid is the result. The equation for the reaction is

$$SO_3 + H_2O \rightarrow H_2SO_4$$

Each mole of SO_3 produces 1 mole of H_2SO_4, which can, in turn, supply 2 moles of hydrogen ions. The gram-equivalent weight of SO_3 is its formula weight divided by 2.

Problem: Calculate the normality of the acidic solution obtained by dissolving 7.6 g of SO_3 in enough water to make 0.250 liter of solution.

The formula weight of SO_3 is 80. The gram-equivalent weight of SO_3 is _____ g.

40

The number of gram-equivalents is _____.

0.19

When 0.19 g-equiv of SO_3 is dissolved in enough water
to make 0.250 liter of solution, the normality is _____.   0.76

Very pure NaOH can be obtained by reacting sodium metal with distilled
water ($2Na + 2H_2O \rightarrow 2NaOH + H_2$). If 4.32 g of Na is reacted and the solution is diluted to 5.00 liters, what is the normality of the solution as a base?

0.0188 N Go to A below
0.0376 N Go to B below
0.0751 N Go to C below

A and C

You are incorrect. This sort of problem must be attacked indirectly. First write
the equation for the reaction that produces the base.

$$2Na + 2H_2O \rightarrow 2NaOH + H_2$$

As you can see, 1 mole of Na produces 1 mole of NaOH in solution. The
gram-equivalent weight of NaOH is the same as the formula weight.
    Because it produces 1 g-equiv of NaOH, 1 mole of Na must also be 1 g-equiv.
The gram-equivalent weight of Na is the same as its formula weight, 22.99.
Armed with this information, go back and work the problem again.

B

Right. The normality is based on the gram-equivalent weight of Na. Even though
it contains no OH^- ions itself, 1 mole of Na produces 1 g-equiv of NaOH. Continue
to the section following the solid line.

Now you are ready to apply the gram-equivalent concept to titrations. You
know that the gram-equivalent is defined so that equal numbers of gram-equivalents of reactants undergo reaction with each other. In the titration of a strong
acid with a strong base, the situation at the neutral point is

g-equiv of acid = g-equiv of base

and

$$(N)(\text{liters}) = (N)(\text{liters})$$

The second equation follows because

$$N = \frac{\text{g-equiv}}{\text{liters}}$$

The equation is sometimes written as

$$N_A \times V_A = N_B \times V_B$$

where V = volume in liters
$\quad\quad N$ = normality
$\quad\quad A$ = acid
$\quad\quad B$ = base

If three of the quantities are known, the fourth can be calculated. Either N_A or N_B is usually the unknown to be determined by a titration. Here is a typical problem.

Problem: In a titration 25.0 ml of acid is equivalent to 32.0 ml of 0.120 N base. What is the normality of the acid?

$$N_A = \frac{N_B \times V_B}{V_A} = \frac{(0.120)(0.032)}{(0.025)} = 0.154$$

Notice that it is not necessary to specify the exact nature of the acid or the base. Moreover, it is usually not necessary to know what chemical species are actually present in the solutions. There are very few H^+ ions in a 0.5 N solution of $HC_2H_3O_2$, but the same amount of base is needed to neutralize it as to neutralize an equal volume of 0.5 N HCl. The latter is completely dissociated into H^+ and Cl^- in aqueous solution.

It is also possible to titrate a solid with a solution. For instance, you might titrate some solid NaOH with an HCl solution. Suppose that the weight of NaOH is 2.0 g. The normality of the HCl is 0.75. What volume of acid will neutralize the base?

At the neutral point, the number of gram-equivalents of acid is equal to _____ *the number of gram-*
_____ of the base. *equivalents*

For the HCl solution, the number of gram-equivalents is given by _____. $\quad\quad N_A \times V_A$

For the solid NaOH, the number of gram-equivalents is the weight (2.0 g) divided by the _____ _____.

The gram-equivalent weight of NaOH is _____ g.

40

The volume of HCl required is _____.

$0.066 \; liter = 66 \; ml$

$$V_A = \frac{2.0 \text{ g}/(40 \text{ g/g-equiv})}{0.75 \text{ g-equiv/liter}}$$

A titration is one operation in the chemical technique of *volumetric analysis.* One advantage of volumetric analysis is that the same standard solution can be used again and again to determine the concentrations of unknown solutions. Most analytical laboratories keep standard solutions of acids and bases on hand, ready for use.

Standard solutions of one concentration can be diluted with water to a new concentration. In the last chapter you learned that the relationship

$$M_1 \times V_1 = M_2 \times V_2$$

is the principle on which the operation is based because the number of moles of solute does not change during the dilution.

The same principle applies to solutions for which the concentration is expressed in gram-equivalents per liter, or normality. The equation is

$$N_1 \times V_1 = N_2 \times V_2$$

Problem: How much water must be added to 150 ml of 0.50 N H_2SO_4 to make a solution that is 0.15 N?

$$V_2 = \frac{(0.50 \; N)(0.150 \text{ liter})}{(0.15 \; N)} = 0.50 \text{ liter} = 500 \text{ ml}$$

Amount of water added $= 500 \text{ ml} - 150 \text{ ml} = 350 \text{ ml}$

To what total volume must 75.0 ml of 1.20 N KOH be diluted in order to make 0.70 N KOH?

55 ml   Go to A below
130 ml   Go to B below
185 ml   Go to C below

A

Wrong. The correct answer is not 55 ml. Perhaps you didn't read the problem carefully enough. You started with 75.0 ml of solution and diluted it. The volume cannot decrease during a dilution; it must increase. Go back and choose a more reasonable answer.

B

Right. If 75.0 ml of 1.20 N KOH is diluted to a total volume of 130 ml, the concentration is 0.70 N. Go on to the paragraph following C.

C

Incorrect. The answer is not 185 ml. If you make a quick check, you'll see that 185 ml is out of bounds. You should always make such a test on your answers. Here's how to do it.

The starting material is 75.0 ml of 1.20 N KOH. You wish to dilute it to 0.70 N. Suppose that you double the volume to 150 ml. What would be the normality? It would be half of the original value, or 0.60 N. That's too dilute. Further dilution to 185 ml would only make it more dilute. The correct answer has to be somewhere between 75.0 ml (no dilution at all!) and 150 ml (too much!).

The exact answer can be found with the aid of the equation

$$N_1 \times V_1 = N_2 \times V_2$$

When you have it, go back and choose another answer.

You have now learned to solve the two principal types of problems in volumetric analysis. In any titration, at the equivalence point,

$$N_A \times V_A = N_B \times V_B$$

or when one of the reactants is a solid,

$$N \times V = \frac{\text{wt of solid}}{\text{g-equiv wt}}$$

The first equation serves for dilution problems as well as for titration problems. The use of gram-equivalent weights and normality is not limited to acids and bases. It can also be applied to oxidizing agents and reducing agents. A discussion of this application, however, is beyond the scope of this book.

These final frames are a brief review of the things you have learned in this section on titrations, gram-equivalents, and normality.

The progressive addition of measured amounts of one reactant to another is called a(n) _____.

titration

The critical observation in a titration is a change in a(n) _____.

indicator

In the titration of a strong base with a strong acid, the indicator changes at the _____ point.

neutral

At the neutral point, equal numbers of _____ _____ of acid and base have reacted with each other.

gram-equivalents

The gram-equivalent weight of an acid or base depends on the number of _____ or _____ ions that it can furnish for reaction.

H^+; OH^-

The formula weight of NaOH is 40. Its gram-equivalent weight is _____ g.

40

The formula weight of $Mg(OH)_2$ is 58.3. Its gram-equivalent weight is _____ g.

29.2

The formula weight of H_2SO_4 is 98. Its gram-equivalent weight in the reaction

$$H_2SO_4 + KOH \rightarrow KHSO_4 + H_2O$$

is _____ g.

98

In the equation g-equiv wt = formula wt/x the x represents _____.

the number of moles of H^+ or OH^- ions supplied by 1 mole of an acid or a base

References

Andrews, D. H., and R. J. Kokes, "Fundamental Chemistry," 2d ed., chap. 14, pp. 380–411, Wiley, New York, 1965.

Gregg, D. C., "Principles of Chemistry," 2d ed., chap. 17, pp. 398–421, Allyn and Bacon, Boston, 1963.

Mahan, B. H., "University Chemistry," chap. 6, pp. 172–222, Addison-Wesley, Reading, Mass., 1965.

Pauling, L., "College Chemistry," 3d ed., sec. 16-4, p. 445, chap. 19, pp. 523–538, Freeman, San Francisco, 1964.

Quagliano, J. V., "Chemistry," 2d ed., chap. 20, pp. 460–486, Prentice-Hall, Englewood Cliffs, N.J., 1963.

Sienko, M. J., and R. A. Plane, "Chemistry," 3d ed., chap. 17, pp. 349–388, McGraw-Hill, New York, 1966.

Sienko, M. J., and R. A. Plane, Chemistry: Principles and Properties, chap. 12, pp. 259–286, McGraw-Hill, New York, 1966.

Sisler, H. H., C. A. VanderWerf, and A. W. Davidson, "College Chemistry: A Systematic Approach," 2d ed., chaps. 14 and 15, pp. 237–286, Macmillan, New York, 1961.

Timm, J. A., "General Chemistry," 4th ed., chaps. 23 and 24, pp. 313–341, McGraw-Hill, New York, 1966.

Self-tests

These tests are designed to measure your understanding of the three chapters of this book. They are not all-inclusive; they do not check every fact in the program. If you do well, however, you may be confident that you know the material.

Chapter 1: chemical equilibrium   The first 10 questions are to be answered true or false. All of them refer to the chemical-reaction system represented by this thermochemical equation:

$$CH_4(g) + 2O_2(g) \rightleftharpoons CO_2(g) + 2H_2O(l) + 212,800 \text{ cal}$$

1. As written, the reaction is exothermic.

2. If 16 g of CH_4 (1.0 mole) is burned in excess O_2, 44 g of CO_2 can be produced.

3. When equilibrium is reached, the concentrations of CO_2 and H_2O will be equal.

4. From the thermochemical equation we can conclude that the point of equilibrium is to the right.

5. The equilibrium condition for the system is

$$K = \frac{[CO_2]}{[CH_4][O_2]}$$

6. If the point of equilibrium for the reaction is far to the right, K will be a large number.

7. If the system is in equilibrium, a decrease in total pressure will cause a shift to the left.

8. If the system is in equilibrium, an increase in temperature will cause a shift to the right.

9. If the system is in equilibrium, addition of a catalyst will cause a shift to the left.

10. If the system is in equilibrium, removal of CO_2 will cause a shift to the right.

The next six questions concern the system represented by the equation

$$CO_2(g) + H_2(g) \rightleftharpoons CO(g) + H_2O(g)$$

At 700°C, the equilibrium constant is 0.53.

11. What is the equilibrium condition for the reaction?

12. Is a mixture which contains 0.20 mole of CO, 0.25 mole of H_2O, 0.42 mole of CO_2, and 0.33 mole of H_2 in a 1.0-liter vessel at equilibrium?

13. If a mixture at equilibrium in a 1.0-liter vessel contains 0.25 mole of CO, 0.50 mole of CO_2, and 0.60 mole of H_2, how much H_2O is in the vessel?

14. Suppose that 0.60 mole of CO_2 and 0.80 mole of H_2 is mixed in a 1.0-liter vessel, how much CO will be present when equilibrium is reached? How much H_2O?

15. At 1000°C, a mixture at equilibrium in a 1.0-liter vessel contains 0.16 mole of CO, 0.25 mole of H_2O, 0.51 mole of CO_2, and 0.11 mole of H_2. What is the equilibrium constant at this temperature?

16. From the values for the equilibrium constant at 700 and 1000°C, can you tell whether the reaction at 700°C is endothermic or exothermic? If so, which is it?

Chapter 2: solutions   The first 15 questions are to be answered true or false.

1. All homogeneous materials are solutions.

2. No heterogeneous materials are solutions.

3. The solubility of solids in water does not depend on the temperature.

4. A saturated solution must always be in equilibrium with undissolved solute.

5. Supersaturated solutions are stable and difficult to separate into their components.

6. The solubility of a gas in a liquid increases if the pressure of the gas is increased.

7. A solution contains 10 g of NaOH (formula wt = 40) and 90 g of H_2O (formula wt = 18). The mole fraction of NaOH is 0.048.

8. The solution in question 7 is 10% NaOH by weight.

9. The equilibrium vapor pressure of a solution is always greater than the equilibrium vapor pressure of the solvent alone.

10. The freezing point of a 0.2 m solution of ethanol (formula wt = 46) is lower than the freezing point of a 0.2 m solution of ethylene glycol (formula wt = 62).

11. The solubility of a solid in a liquid is increased by stirring.

12. Oxygen and nitrogen can be separated by fractional distillation.

13. Newly synthesized organic compounds are often purified by crystallization from a suitable solvent.

14. Molarity (M) and formality (F) are often used interchangeably.

15. The molarity of a solution may change with a change in the temperature of the solution.

The next three questions concern the concentrated nitric acid sold by chemical supply houses. It contains 70.0% HNO_3 (formula wt $= 63$) by weight, and its density is 1.41 g/ml.

16. What is the molarity of the solution?

17. What is the molality of the solution?

18. How many milliliters of 5.0% HNO_3 can be prepared by diluting 25 ml of concentrated HNO_3 with water?

Chapter 3: solutions of electrolytes   The first 10 questions are to be answered true or false.

1. Solutions of electrolytes show abnormally large freezing-point depressions.

2. Electrolytic conductivity always involves a chemical change.

3. The percent dissociation of weak electrolytes increases with increasing concentration.

4. The freezing-point depression of a 1 m solution of KCl is less than $3.72°C$ because of interionic attraction.

5. An acidic solution contains more positive ions than negative ions.

6. From the Brønsted-Lowry viewpoint, water acts as a base in this reaction: $CN^- + H_2O \rightleftharpoons HCN + OH^-$.

7. In pure water and all aqueous solutions at $25°C$, $[H^+][OH^-] = 1 \times 10^{-14}$.

8. 25 ml of 0.1 M H_2SO_4 will exactly neutralize 25 ml of 0.1 M KOH.

9. The pH of 0.01 M HNO_3 is 2.

10. The normality of H_2SO_4 solutions is always twice the molarity.

The next seven questions concern a solution prepared by dissolving 0.80 g of pure NaOH (formula wt $= 40$) in enough water to make exactly 100 ml of solution.

11. What is the molarity of the solution?

12. What is the normality of the solution?

13. What is the OH^- concentration of the solution?

14. What is the H^+ concentration of the solution?

15. What is the pH of the solution?

16. What is the pOH of the solution?

17. How much $0.15\ N$ HCl is required to neutralize 36 ml of this NaOH solution?

When Na_2CO_3 (formula wt $= 106$) is neutralized with HCl, the reaction is $CO_3^= + 2H^+ \rightleftharpoons H_2O + CO_2$. The next four questions concern this reaction.

18. What is the gram-equivalent weight of Na_2CO_3?

19. What is the gram-equivalent weight of HCl?

20. What volume of $0.12\ N$ HCl is needed to neutralize 0.083 g of Na_2CO_3?

21. What volume of $0.05\ N$ Na_2CO_3 can be prepared by dissolving 0.53 g in water?

Answers

Chapter 1

1. True	2. True	3. False
4. False	5. False	6. True
7. True	8. False	9. False
10. True	11. $K = \dfrac{[CO][H_2O]}{[CO_2][H_2]}$	12. No
13. 0.64 mole	14. 0.29 mole of each	15. 0.71
16. Yes; endothermic		

Chapter 2

1. False	2. True	3. False
4. False	5. False	6. True
7. True	8. True	9. False
10. False	11. False	12. True
13. True	14. True	15. True
16. 15.7	17. 37.0	18. 350 ml

Chapter 3

1. True	2. True	3. False
4. True	5. False	6. False
7. True	8. False	9. True
10. False	11. 0.20	12. 0.20
13. 0.20 mole/liter	14. 5×10^{-14} mole/liter	15. 13.3
16. 0.7	17. 48 ml	18. 53 g
19. 36.5 g	20. 13 ml	21. 200 ml

appendix

1 Atomic weights

ATOMIC WEIGHTS

Name	Symbol	Atomic number	Atomic weight	Name	Symbol	Atomic number	Atomic weight
Actinium	Ac	89	[227]*	Chromium	Cr	24	51.996
Aluminum	Al	13	26.9815	Cobalt	Co	27	58.9332
Americium	Am	95	[243]	Copper	Cu	29	63.546
Antimony	Sb	51	121.75	Curium	Cm	96	[247]
Argon	Ar	18	39.948	Dysprosium	Dy	66	162.50
Arsenic	As	33	74.9216	Einsteinium	Es	99	[254]
Astatine	At	85	[210]	Erbium	Er	68	167.26
Barium	Ba	56	137.34	Europium	Eu	63	151.96
Berkelium	Bk	97	[249]	Fermium	Fm	100	[253]
Beryllium	Be	4	9.0122	Fluorine	F	9	18.9984
Bismuth	Bi	83	208.980	Francium	Fr	87	[223]
Boron	B	5	10.811	Gadolinium	Gd	64	157.25
Bromine	Br	35	79.904	Gallium	Ga	31	69.72
Cadmium	Cd	48	112.40	Germanium	Ge	32	72.59
Calcium	Ca	20	40.08	Gold	Au	79	196.967
Californium	Cf	98	[251]	Hafnium	Hf	72	178.49
Carbon	C	6	12.01115	Helium	He	2	4.0026
Cerium	Ce	58	140.12	Holmium	Ho	67	164.930
Cesium	Cs	55	132.905	Hydrogen	H	1	1.00797
Chlorine	Cl	17	35.453	Indium	In	49	114.82

* Values in brackets are mass numbers of longest-lived or best-known isotopes.

Name	Symbol	Atomic number	Atomic weight	Name	Symbol	Atomic number	Atomic weight
Iodine	I	53	126.9044	Radium	Ra	88	[226]
Iridium	Ir	77	192.2	Radon	Rn	86	[222]
Iron	Fe	26	55.847	Rhenium	Re	75	186.2
Krypton	Kr	36	83.80	Rhodium	Rh	45	102.905
Lanthanum	La	57	138.91	Rubidium	Rb	37	85.47
Lawrencium	Lw	103	[257]	Ruthenium	Ru	44	101.07
Lead	Pb	82	207.19	Samarium	Sm	62	150.35
Lithium	Li	3	6.939	Scandium	Sc	21	44.956
Lutetium	Lu	71	174.97	Selenium	Se	34	78.96
Magnesium	Mg	12	24.312	Silicon	Si	14	28.086
Manganese	Mn	25	54.9380	Silver	Ag	47	107.868
Mendelevium	Md	101	[256]	Sodium	Na	11	22.9898
Mercury	Hg	80	200.59	Strontium	Sr	38	87.62
Molybdenum	Mo	42	95.94	Sulfur	S	16	32.064
Neodymium	Nd	60	144.24	Tantalum	Ta	73	180.948
Neon	Ne	10	20.183	Technetium	Tc	43	[99]
Neptunium	Np	93	[237]	Tellurium	Te	52	127.60
Nickel	Ni	28	58.71	Terbium	Tb	65	158.924
Niobium	Nb	41	92.906	Thallium	Tl	81	204.37
Nitrogen	N	7	14.0067	Thorium	Th	90	232.038
Nobelium	No	102	[254]	Thulium	Tm	69	168.934
Osmium	Os	76	190.2	Tin	Sn	50	118.69
Oxygen	O	8	15.9994	Titanium	Ti	22	47.90
Palladium	Pd	46	106.4	Tungsten	W	74	183.85
Phosphorus	P	15	30.9738	Uranium	U	92	238.03
Platinum	Pt	78	195.09	Vanadium	V	23	50.942
Plutonium	Pu	94	[242]	Xenon	Xe	54	131.30
Polonium	Po	84	[210]	Ytterbium	Yb	70	173.04
Potassium	K	19	39.102	Yttrium	Y	39	88.905
Praseodymium	Pr	59	140.907	Zinc	Zn	30	65.37
Promethium	Pm	61	[145]	Zirconium	Zr	40	91.22
Protactinium	Pa	91	[231]				

2 Logarithms

The logarithm of a number is the power to which 10 must be raised to equal the number. For example, the logarithm (log) of 1,000 (or 10^3) is 3. The log of 0.01 (or 10^{-2}) is -2. Since most numbers are not even powers of 10, their logarithms are not so easy to find. These logs are found from log tables such as the one below.

To find the logarithm of 4.8, find 4 in the first column, and then go across to the column headed by 0.8. The log of 4.8 is 0.681. Logs of numbers smaller than 1.0 or larger than 9.9 are found after they are written in exponential form to give a number between 1.0 and 9.9 multiplied by a power of 10. For instance, the number 390 becomes 3.9×10^2.

The logarithm of a product is equal to the sum of the logarithms of the factors (for example, $\log (a \times b) = \log a + \log b$). So,

$$\begin{aligned} \log (3.9 \times 10^2) &= \log 3.9 + \log 10^2 \\ &= 0.591 + 2 \\ &= 2.591 \end{aligned}$$

Occasionally you will want to find the number from its logarithm. The number is often called the antilogarithm. Antilogarithms are found by using the table in reverse. For example, if the logarithm of a number is 0.38, the number is 2.4.

LOGARITHMS

	0.0	0.1	0.2	0.3	0.4	0.5	0.6	0.7	0.8	0.9
1	000	041	079	114	146	176	204	230	255	279
2	301	322	342	362	380	398	415	431	447	462
3	477	491	505	519	532	544	556	568	580	591
4	602	613	623	634	644	653	663	672	681	690
5	699	708	716	724	732	740	748	756	763	771
6	778	785	792	799	806	813	820	826	833	839
7	845	851	857	863	869	875	881	887	892	898
8	903	909	914	919	924	929	935	940	945	949
9	954	959	964	969	973	978	982	987	991	996

3 Units and conversion factors

1 meter (m) = 39.4 inches, U.S. (in.)

1 meter (m) = 100 centimeters (cm)

1 centimeter (cm) = 0.394 U.S. in.

1 liter (l) = 1.06 quarts, U.S., liquid (qt)

1 liter (l) = 1,000 milliliters (ml)

1 milliliter (ml) = 1 cubic centimeter (cc)

1 atomic mass unit (amu) = 1.66×10^{-24} grams (g)

1 pound, avoir. (lb) = 453.6 grams (g)

1 kilogram (kg) = 1,000 grams (g)

1 faraday = 96,500 coulombs, absolute

index